PRESCHOOL

Illustrations by Michele Ackerman, Dan Andreasen, Gabriele Antonini, Martha Avilés, Michelle Berg, Robin Boyer, Laurie Brackenbury, Kathi Ember, Marina Fedotova, Louise Gardner, Daniel Howarth, Angela Jarecki, Agnieszka Jatkowska, Holly Jones, Barbara Lanza, Jane Maday, Robert Masheris, Kathleen McCord, David Merrell, Chris Moroney, Nicholas Myers, Burgandy Nilles, Lance Raichert, Christine Schneider, Susan Spellman, Peggy Tagel, George Ulrich, Tim Warren, Ted Williams, and David Wojtowycz

Photography © Art Explosion, Artville, Brand X, Corbis, Dreamstime, Getty Images, Image Club, iStock Photo, Jupiter Images Unlimited, Media Bakery, Photodisc, Shutterstock.com, Stockbyte, and Thinkstock
Additional Photography by Brian Warling Photography and Siede Preis Photography

Customer Service: 1-800-595-8484 or customer_service@pilbooks.com

www.pilbooks.com

p i kids is a trademark of Publications International, Ltd.,
and is registered in the United States.
Brain Games is a trademark of Publications International, Ltd.

8 7 6 5 4 3 2 1

Manufactured in USA.

ISBN-10: 1-4508-5665-9
ISBN-13: 978-1-4508-5665-2

 publications international, ltd.

Welcome to Brain Games!

Dear Parents,

Are you ready to help build your child's brainpower? This Brain Games workbook will do just that! A variety of curriculum-based topics provide a wonderful opportunity to learn new things. In the front of the book, you will find simple, introductory exercises. As you work your way toward the back of the book, the questions will gradually become more challenging. Along the way, the 1001 questions cover eight important areas:

- Language arts
- Math
- Science
- Social sciences
- Fine arts
- Physical development
- Emotional development
- Foreign language

To make the most of this book, please keep these suggestions in mind:

- Choose a learning time when your child is rested and alert.
- Focus on just one question at a time.
- Read the question aloud.
- Give your child time to answer each question without your help. When you need to, work together to compare answers to the answer keys in the back of the book.
- This is a big book with a lot of questions! Take a break as often as needed.
- Be positive and encouraging. Learning should be fun!

Hey, kids!

Are you ready to show what you know and learn new things, too?

Great! All you need is something to write with and a quiet place where you can concentrate.

Get set to learn about all of these terrific things:

✔ Letters & words
✔ Numbers & counting
✔ Adding & subtracting
✔ Shapes
✔ Colors
✔ Plants
✔ Animals
✔ People
✔ Planets

And much, much more!

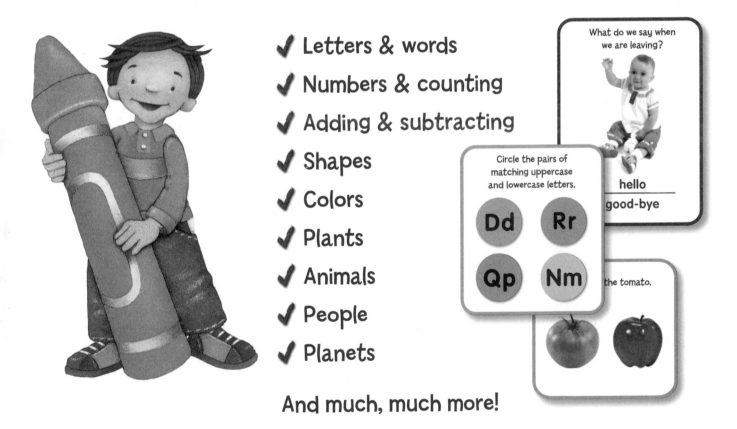

What do we say when we are leaving?

hello
good-bye

Circle the pairs of matching uppercase and lowercase letters.

Dd   Rr

Qp   Nm

the tomato.

Are you ready? Get set...
Let's GO!

Trace and write the letters.

Trace and write the letters.

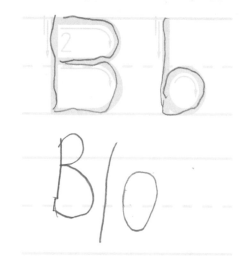

Trace and write the letters.

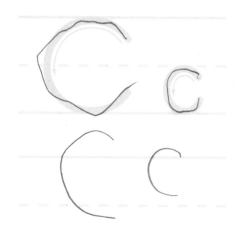

Trace and write the letters.

Match each picture to its beginning letter.

A   **B**   **C**   **D**

Answers on page 258.

Trace and write the letters.

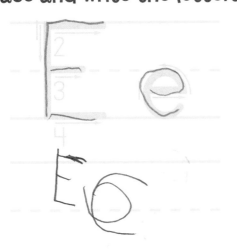

Trace and write the letters.

Draw a line to connect the letters.

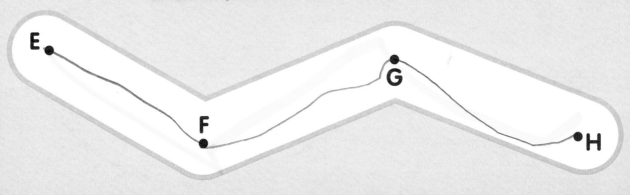

Trace and write the letters.

Trace and write the letters.

Answers on page 258.

Trace and write the letters.

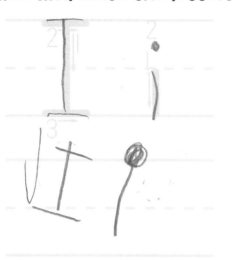

Trace and write the letters.

Draw a line to connect the letters.

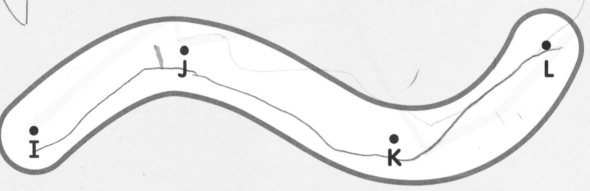

Trace and write the letters.

Trace and write the letters.

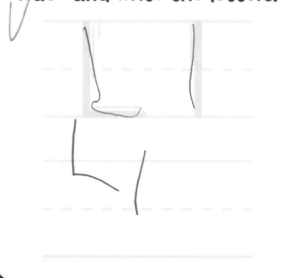

Answers on page 258.

Trace and write the letters.

Trace and write the letters.

Trace and write the letters.

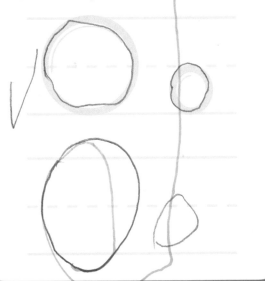

Trace and write the letters.

Match each picture to its beginning letter.

M   **N**   **O**   **P**

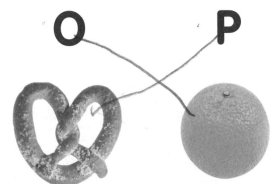

Trace and write the letters.

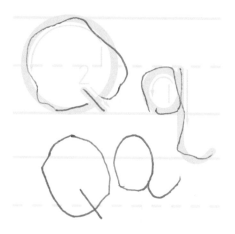

Trace and write the letters.

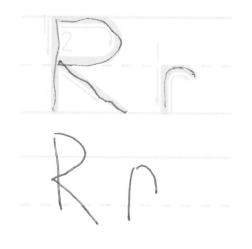

Trace and write the letters.

Trace and write the letters.

Match each picture to its beginning letter.

Q   R   S   T

8

Answers on page 259

Draw a line to connect the letters.

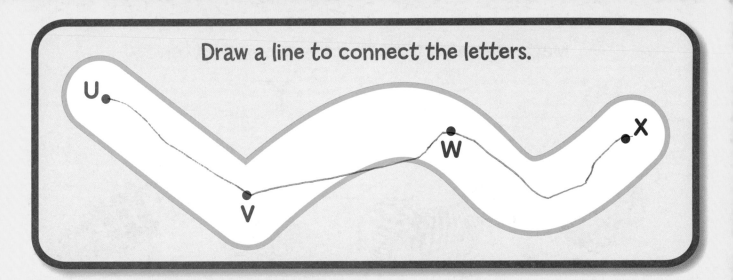

Trace and write the letters.

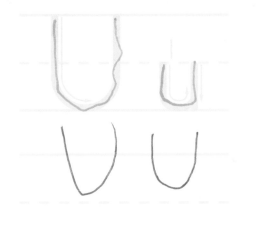

Trace and write the letters.

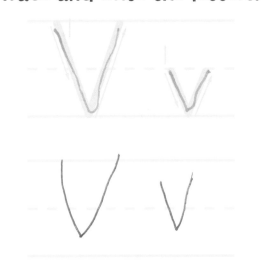

Trace and write the letters.

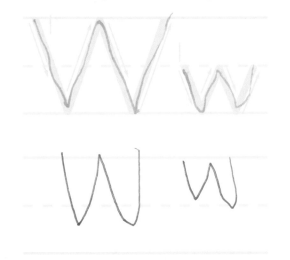

Trace and write the letters.

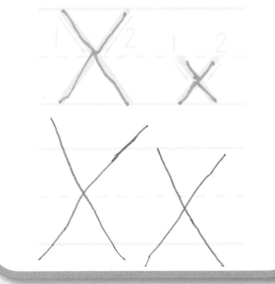

Answers on page 259.

Match each picture to its beginning letter.

W   X   Y   Z

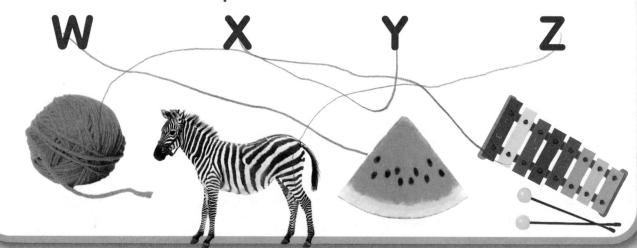

Trace and write the letters.

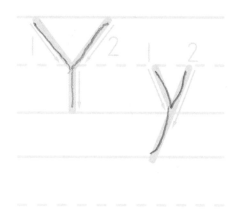

Trace and write the letters.

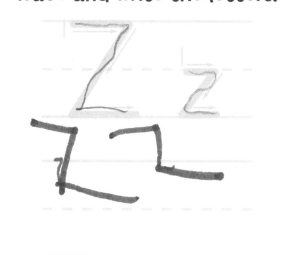

Draw a line to connect the letters.

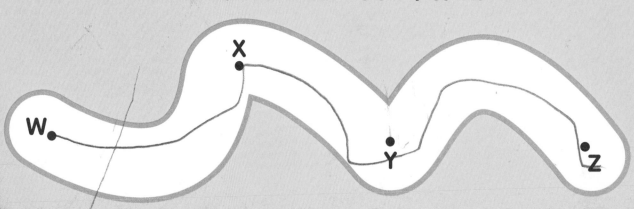

Answers on page 259

Trace and write the number.

1

1

Trace and write the number.

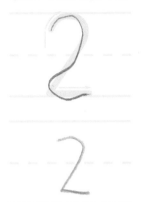

2

2

Trace and write the number.

3

3

How many fingers are held up in this picture?

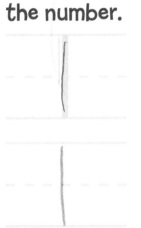

1

How many yo-yos? Circle the correct number.

1 2 3 4 5

Which numbers come next?

How many tigers are there?

Answers on page 259.

Trace and write the number.

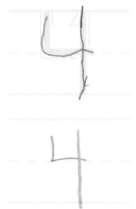

4

4

Trace and write the number.

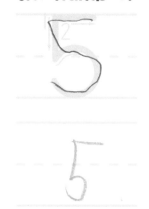

5

5

Trace and write the number.

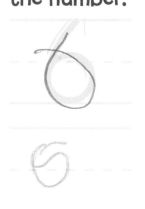

6

6

How many fingers are held up in this picture?

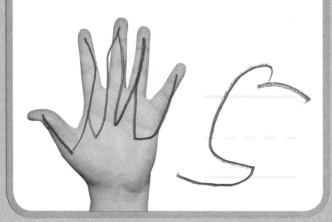

5

How many birds are in the tree?

0

Which number comes next?

1 2 3 4

How many frogs are there?

4

Answers on page 260.

Trace and write the number.

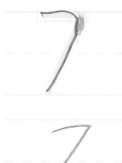

7

7

Trace and write the number.

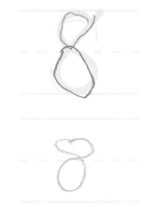

8

8

How many tops are there?

7

Trace and write the number.

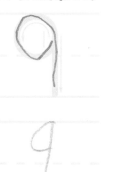

9

9

Trace and write the number.

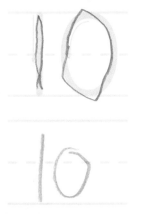

10

10

How many watermelon slices do you see?

What should you say if you accidentally burp?

excuse me **please**

Follow the alphabet to connect the dots.

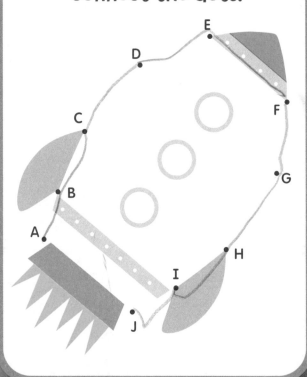

Fill in the shapes that have the letter **D**. What is it?

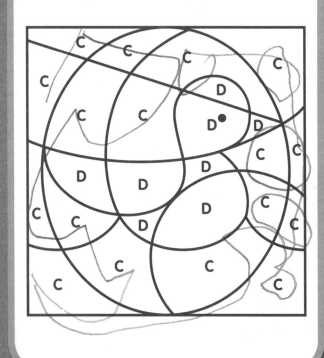

Circle the man.

Answers on page 260.

Circle the animal that roars.

How many sea stars?
Circle the correct number.

1 2 3 4 5

Which one do you use to wash your hands?

Find and circle the word **bag**.

c q b x
f t a d
j w g i
n p z y

Circle the oldest one.

How many fingers are held up in this picture?

Which person is wearing glasses?

Circle the animal that oinks.

Find and circle the word **hid**.

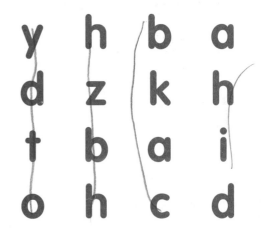

y h b a

d z k h

t b a i

o h c d

Fill in the missing number.

1 2 3 4 5 6

Answers on page 261.

How many buttons can you find on the bear?

5

Is it hot or cold in this picture?

hot   cold

Which letter comes next? Use the picture to help.

ab Db

Fill in the shapes that have the letter F. What is it?

Follow the alphabet to connect the dots.

How many circles can you find?

Which letter comes next? Use the picture to help.

bc bc

Connect the dots.

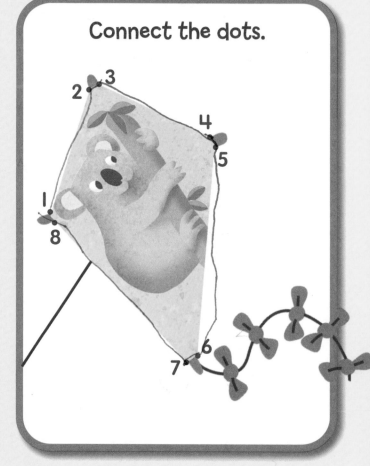

18

Answers on page 261.

Circle the animal that meows.

How many soccer balls?
Circle the correct number.

1 2 3 4 5

How many fingers are held up in this picture?

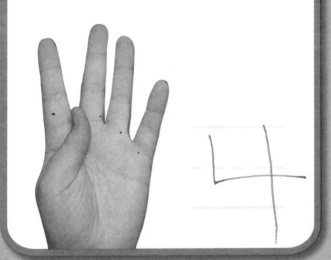

What do you wash after using the bathroom?

hands
face

Circle the creature that made this web.

Answers on page 261.

Circle the body part you use to hear.

Circle the fox.

What is the opposite of sad?

Circle the one that's shaped like a triangle.

Match the food to its color.

purple red yellow

Answers on page 262.

Circle the animal that moos.

How many yellow dogs are there?

Answers on page 262.

How many petals are on the flower?

8

Circle the animal that barks.

Which letter comes next? Use the picture to help.

de

Follow the alphabet to connect the dots.

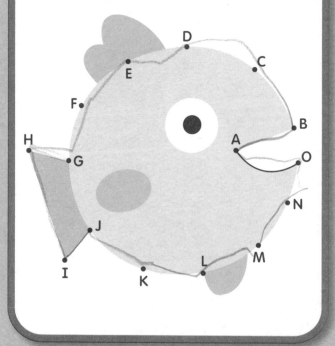

Answers on page 262.

Find and circle the word **car**.

z c a r
w k b e
h p b u
i a f d

Is the weather hot or cold in this picture?

(hot)   cold

How many socks? Circle the correct number.

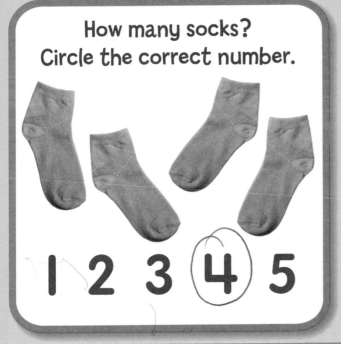

1 2 3 (4) 5

Is it summer or winter in this picture?

summer   (winter)

Circle the animal that lives in the water.

Circle the uppercase letters.

f B d

H G t

Fill in the triangles.

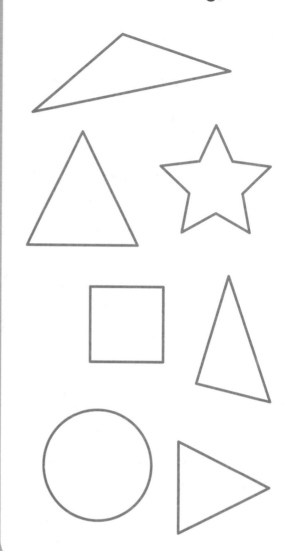

Which one is orange?

Which number comes next?

3 4 5

Match the food to its color.

yellow blue red

Answers on page 263.

How many animals have spots?

3

How many bells are there?

Which letter comes next?
Use the picture to help.

ef

Circle the lowercase letters.

I B d
b g Q

Circle the baby who has green eyes.

What shape is the yo-yo?

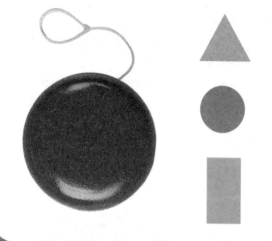

Which one is white?

Circle the one that's shaped like a square.

Answers on page 263.

Which letter comes next? Use the picture to help.

f g

Is it windy or calm in this picture?

windy   calm

Fill in the shapes that have the letter W. What is it?

Which one means hello in Spanish?

adiós

hola

Answers on page 263.

Fill in the shapes that have the letter **S**. What is it?

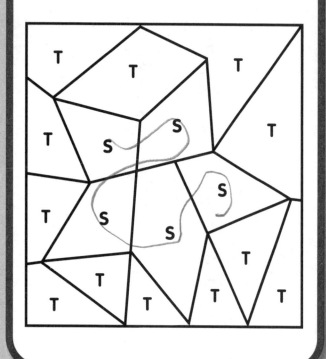

Which letter comes next? Use the picture to help.

Connect the dots.

Put an **X** on each pair that does not have matching uppercase and lowercase letters.

Yo   Tt

Aa   Nn

28

Answers on page 264.

Circle the one that's shaped like a circle.

How many sea horses? Circle the correct number.

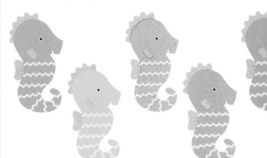

1 2 3 4 5

Which person is a girl?

Which one is black?

Circle the animals that have four legs.

Answers on page 264.

Match the food to its color.

green   red   orange

Find and circle the word **sun**.

u	k	y	s
a	c	d	u
e	g	h	n
o	b	p	d

Circle the uppercase letters.

f   Z   e
Q   M   h

Which person is a boy?

Circle the animal that is a mammal.

Answers on page 264.

Who is sad?

Fill in the circles.

Which letter comes next? Use the picture to help.

i j

Circle the pairs of matching uppercase and lowercase letters.

Dd   Rr

Qp   Nm

Answers on page 264.

What shape is the badge?

Which number comes next?

Which one is black?

What do we say when we are leaving?

hello

_____

good-bye

Circle the uppercase letters.

32

Answers on page 265.

Which one is the mother?

Which animal has horns?

Find and circle the word **bat**.

p w b n
s y f q
v a h s
c b a t

Which one of these is not an insect?

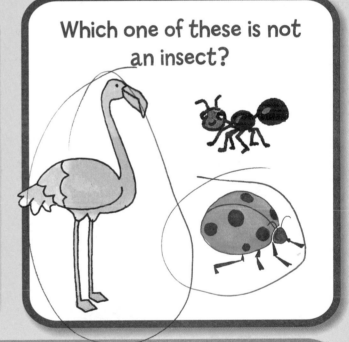

How many quails do you see?

Is the cat crying or smiling?

crying   smiling

Which letter comes next? Use the picture to help.

j k

Circle the pairs of matching uppercase and lowercase letters.

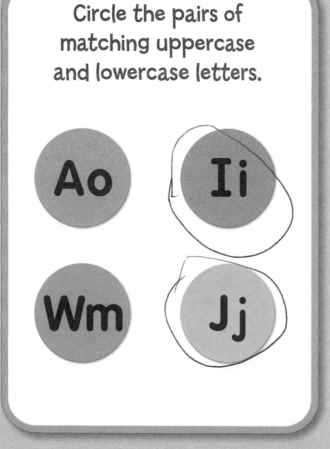

Ao   Ii

Wm   Jj

Which one means **I love you** in Spanish?

te amo   me llamo

Answers on page 265.

How many squirrels do you see?

6

How many yellow things do you see?

3

How many birds are there?

3

Which letter comes next? Use the picture to help.

k l

Put an **X** on each pair that does not have matching uppercase and lowercase letters.

Li   Cc

Ee   Bc

Connect the dots.

1
2
3
7
4
6
5

Match the uppercase and lowercase letters.

A   b

B   e

C   a

D   d

E   c

Answers on page 266.

What shape is the tent?

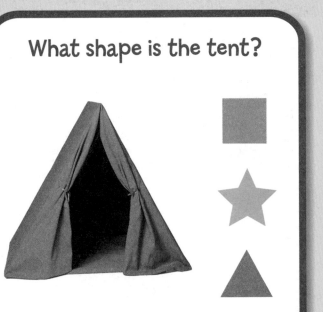

Circle the animal that says baa.

Fill in the squares.

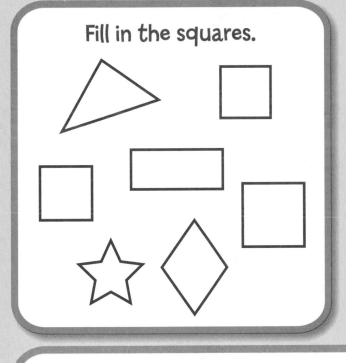

Which one is the grandmother?

How many rockets do you see?

Answers on page 266.

How many green things do you see?

How many helicopters are there?

38

Find and circle the word **leg**.

h	k	b	a
b	l	e	g
a	g	u	d
c	w	l	o

Which one is pink?

How many roller coaster cars are yellow?

Circle the uppercase letters.

p E l

R I t

Which one is slower?

Answers on page 266.

How many fingers are held up in this picture?

Which letter comes next? Use the picture to help.

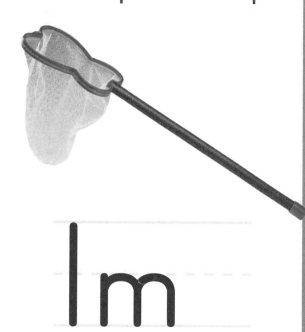

l m

Connect the dots.

Match the uppercase and lowercase letters.

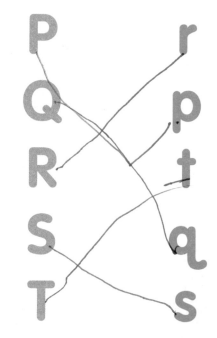

P
Q
R
S
T

r
p
t
q
s

Which person has blond hair?

Which one is brown?

Which one is the sister?

Find and circle the word **win**.

w	d	e	h
i	c	t	a
n	u	z	g
p	v	k	w

Fill in the missing number.

Answers on page 267.

How many green trucks do you see?

Which letter comes next? Use the picture to help.

no

Fill in the shapes that have the letter **B**. What is it?

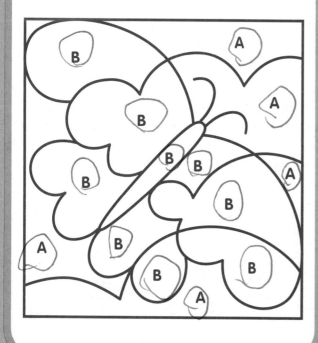

Which one means **good-bye** in Spanish?

hola

adiós

42

Answers on page 267.

How many black things do you see?

Which letter comes next? Use the picture to help.

op

Follow the alphabet to connect the dots.

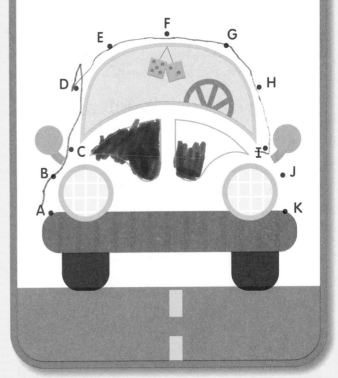

Find and circle the word **hen**.

q e i c
a w h u
y s e g
d i n t

Who is happy?

Who is surprised?

Which one is green?

Circle the uppercase letters.

b F r
k t D

Answers on page 268.

Which letter comes next? Use the picture to help.

pq

Follow the alphabet to connect the dots.

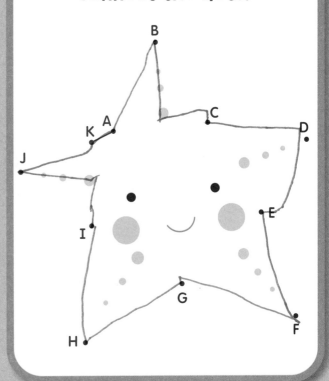

Which one means **friend** in Spanish?

amigo

el gato

Circle the pairs of matching uppercase and lowercase letters.

Gg   Tt

Lv   Co

How many trucks are there?

Match the uppercase and lowercase letters.

F h
G g
H i
I f
J j

How many fingers are held up in this picture?

46

Answers on page 268.

Who is mad?

How many koalas do you see?

Which one means **good morning** in Spanish?

 **buenos días**

buenas noches

Connect the dots.

Which person has black hair?

Find and circle the word **one**.

a n b c
w f i a
t v s h
o n e y

Which animal likes cheese?

Which one is the grandfather?

Circle the animal that neighs.

Answers on page 269.

Put an **X** on each pair that does not have matching uppercase and lowercase letters.

Hh **Mn**

Ww **Xv**

Follow the alphabet to connect the dots.

Circle the person who has brown eyes.

How many apples are in the tree?

Circle the lowercase letters.

j d D P e T

Match the uppercase and lowercase letters.

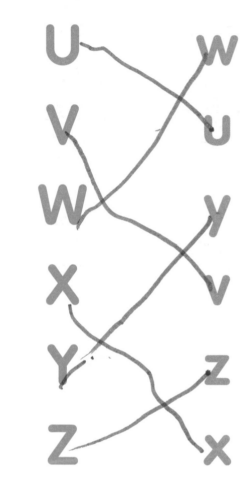

U   w
V   u
W   y
X   v
Y   z
Z   x

Circle the body part you eat with.

Match the food to its color.

green   orange   blue

Which number comes next?

56

50

What do we say if we hurt someone's feelings?

sorry   **thank you**

Which letter comes next? Use the picture to help.

q r

Put an X on each pair that does not have matching uppercase and lowercase letters.

 Xx   Yz

 Vw   Uu

How many snowflakes? Circle the correct number.

6 ⑦ 8 9 10

Which letter comes next? Use the picture to help.

r s ___

Which one means please in Spanish?

 el cerdo

por favor

Follow the alphabet to connect the dots.

Put an X on each pair that does not have matching uppercase and lowercase letters.

Vv   Ap

Cb   Ff

Answers on page 270.

Is it raining or snowing in this picture?

raining   snowing

Find and circle the word **pet**.

k h x z
p b d e
e q i t
t f m o

Which one is asleep?

Which person is using crutches?

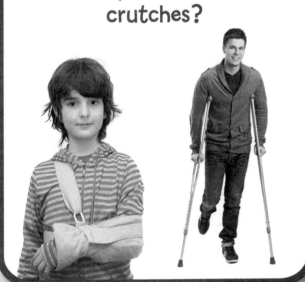

Fill in the missing number.

5   6   7   8   9

Answers on page 270.

Is the bunny happy or angry?

happy   angry

Connect the dots.

How many red wagons do you see?

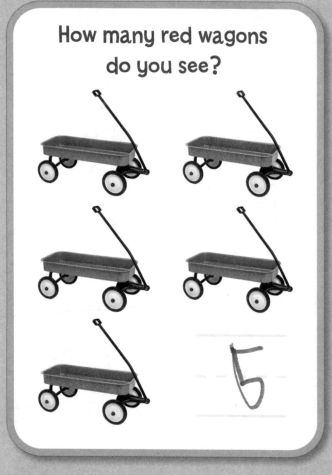

5

Which letter comes next? Use the picture to help.

t u

Answers on page 270.

Circle the one that's shaped like a diamond.

Fill in the stars.

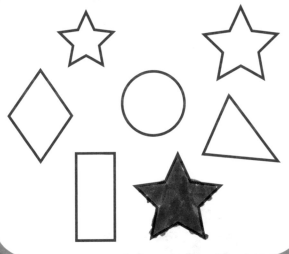

Follow the alphabet to connect the dots.

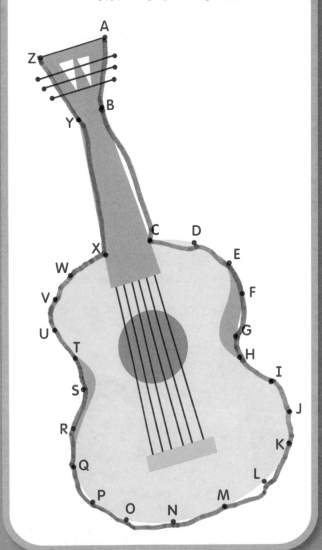

Match the food to its color.

blue **yellow** **red**

Which one is blue?

Circle the animal that has feathers.

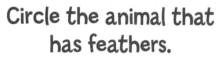

Find and circle the word **bed**.

e b f d
j w v a
b e d c
k a s h

Which person wears braces?

Which animal is black and white?

Fill in the missing number.

3   4   ?   6   7

Answers on page 271.

How many leaves?
Circle the correct number.

6 7 8 9 10

Which letter comes next?
Use the picture to help.

uv

How many red things do you see?

Which one is the son?

Find and circle the word **two**.

d   t   h   l

x   w   k   p

y   o   f   j

g   c   v   b

Circle the imaginary animal.

Match the food to its color.

green   red   orange

Which one is yellow?

What shape is the lollipop?

58

Answers on page 271.

Which number comes next?

6 7 8

Fill in the diamonds.

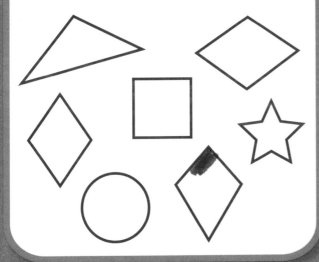

Match the food to its color.

black   yellow   red

Follow the alphabet to connect the dots.

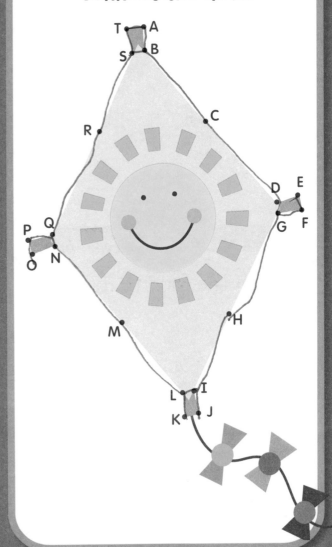

Circle the lowercase letters.

n   I   g

N   O   K

Circle the one that's shaped like a star.

Match the food to its color.

green   red   white

What should we say when we see someone?

hello
_____

good-bye

Which number comes next?

7 8 ⦰

Find and circle the word mitt.

o e d z
l j a o
m i t t
s c k e

Answers on page 272.

Which person has a cast?

What two shapes make this ice-cream cone?

Which one do you use to comb your hair?

Which one is the brother?

Which food should the rabbit eat?

Answers on page 272.

How many orange things do you see?

Which letter comes next?
Use the picture to help.

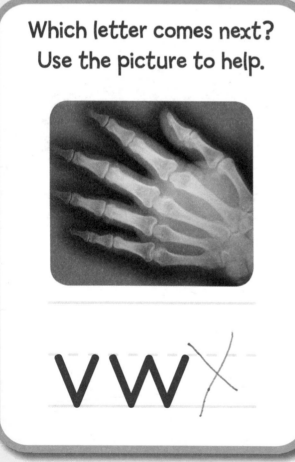

V W X

Connect the dots.

62

Answers on page 272.

Which one is the daughter?

Which one is red?

Find and circle the word **job**.

z p w h
b y a c
e d v e
j o b l

What shape is the door?

Circle the animal that trumpets.

Circle the lowercase letters.

q R u
G W a

Answers on page 272.

Match the uppercase and lowercase letters.

K m

L k

M n

N o

O l

Which one means **thank you** in Spanish?

gracias

adiós

How many crackers? Circle the correct number.

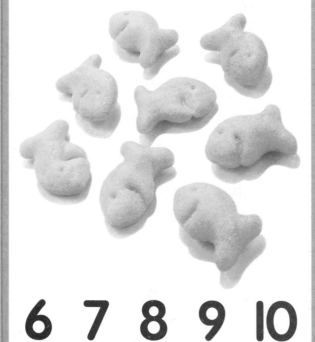

6 7 8 9 10

Fill in the shapes that have the letter **L**. What is it?

64

Answers on page 273.

Find and circle the word **his**.

b e z h
c h i s
u z l y
w k p u

Which one is tired?

Is it fall or spring in this picture?

fall   spring

Which one is the dog?

Fill in the missing number.

4 5 6 __ 8 9

Find and circle the word **egg**.

f	n	l	e
i	u	o	g
n	v	d	g
m	w	n	z

Circle the uppercase letters.

C P O

D Q a

How many cupcakes? Circle the correct number.

6 7 8 9 10

Underline the words that begin with the letter **B**.

This is the best book about bumblebees.

Which one is purple?

Answers on page 273.

Circle the one that begins with the letter **A**.

Circle the woman.

Which letter comes next? Use the picture to help.

WX

Fill in the shapes that have the letter **H**. What is it?

G	G		G	
G			H	G
		H	H	G
G		H		H	
G				G
G			G	
G				H	G
	G			G	G
G		H		G	G

Which letter comes next? Use the picture to help.

x y ___

Connect the dots.

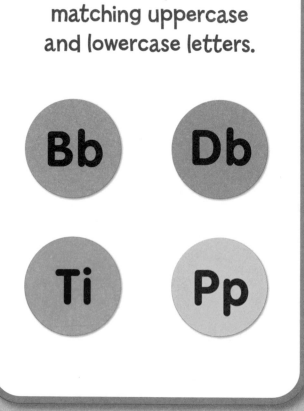

How many fingers are held up in this picture?

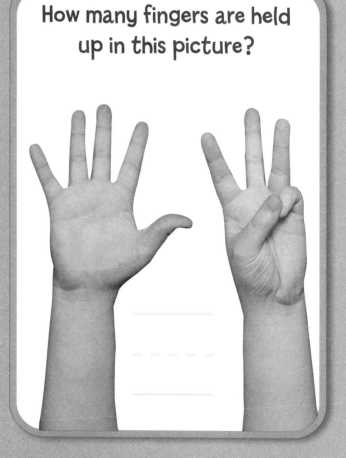

Circle the pairs of matching uppercase and lowercase letters.

Bb   Db

Ti   Pp

Answers on page 274.

Find and circle the word **cup**.

a f i t
m c s k
r u l d
z p w s

Circle the person with blue eyes.

Is it fall or spring in this picture?

fall   **spring**

Which one means **good night** in Spanish?

 **buenas noches**

estrella

How many grasshoppers? Circle the correct number.

1   2   3   4   5   6   7   8   9   10

Find and circle the word **dot**.

d o t g
p i e b
g p z c
h t k s

Circle the group that has more.

Which one is awake?

Find and circle 2 letter **G**s in this picture.

Circle the group that has more.

70

Answers on page 274.

How many fingers are held up in this picture?

Circle the pairs of matching uppercase and lowercase letters.

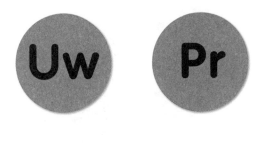

Uw   Pr

Ll   Qq

Fill in the shapes that have the letter **T**. What is it?

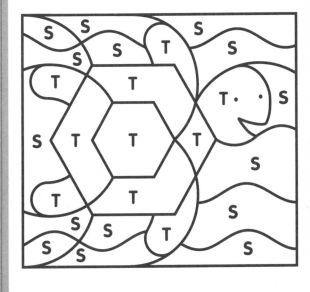

Connect the dots.

Answers on page 274.

What is this?
Write its first letter.

Follow the alphabet to connect the dots.

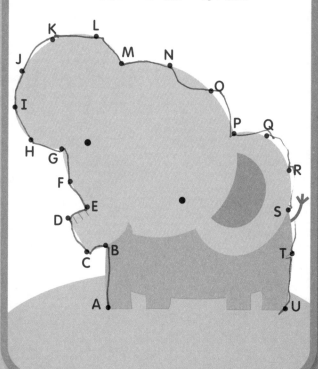

Fill in the shapes that have the letter **K**. What is it?

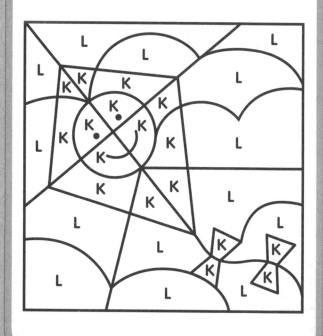

Connect the two things that go together.

Answers on page 275.

Circle the letter that is a vowel.

J G

S

I R

What meal do you eat after lunch?

breakfast   dinner

Are there more zebras or buses? Circle the answer.

zebras

buses

Find and circle the word **her**.

h	k	a	u
e	v	s	p
r	t	y	g
d	e	o	f

Draw a triangle.

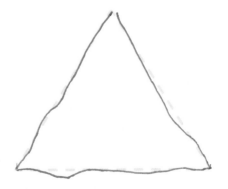

Fill in the shapes to finish the pattern.

How many umbrellas can you find in this picture?

Answers on page 275.

Color the spaces that have the number 5.

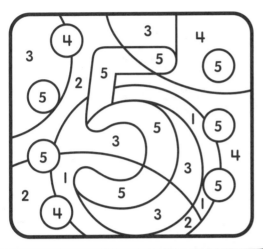

Match the shoe to the right body part.

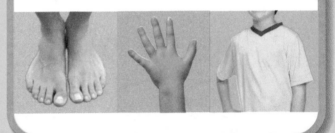

Circle the one who wears a crown.

Are these shapes all triangles?

yes **no**

Trace the word.

orange

Find and circle the word **three**.

```
d  y  w  m  r
r  p  c  f  n
t  h  r  e  e
z  k  e  o  q
b  g  v  u  l
```

Circle the car that holds more people.

Who lives in the igloo?

What meal do you eat after breakfast?

lunch   dinner

How many candles have stripes?

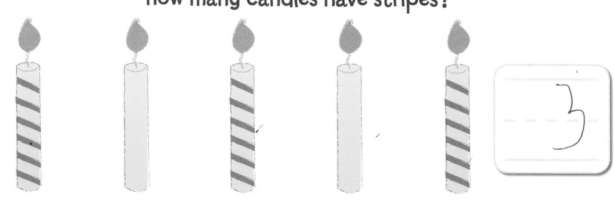

Put an **X** on the animal that is not a reptile.

Which color is at the top of the rainbow?

violet   red   yellow

Fill in the shapes that have the letter **U**. What is it?

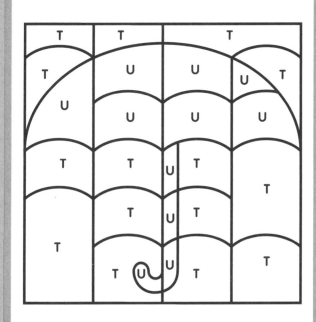

Which person delivers the mail?

Connect the two things that go together.

Circle the group that has more.

What sound does the letter D make? Does this picture begin with the letter D?

yes

no

Where can we find books?

78

Answers on page 276.

Find and circle 5 letter **H**s in this picture.

How many of these vehicles have four wheels?

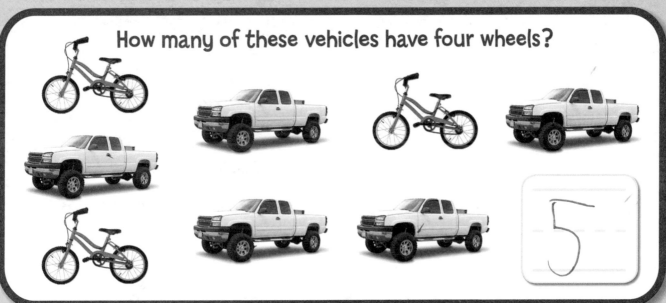

Circle the things that begin with the letter **S.**

Answers on page 276.

Find and circle 4 letter **I**s in this picture.

Connect the dots.

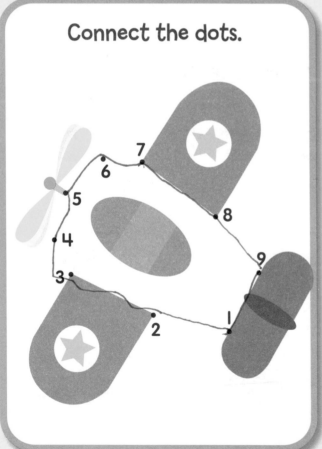

Put an **X** on the one that is different.

Answers on page 277.

Is the hat on or off
the dog's head?

on   off

Circle the group
that has more.

Circle the fisherman who
caught the most fish.

Circle the letter that
is a vowel.

Circle the one that is hotter.

Answers on page 277.

How many acorns are there?

What do you brush before you go to bed?

feet

teeth

Match the shirt to the right body part.

Circle the one that is empty.

Trace the word.

white

82

Answers on page 277.

How many apples are red?

Put an **X** on the one that is different.

Which helper puts out fires?

What sound does the letter **F** make? Does this picture begin with the letter **F**?

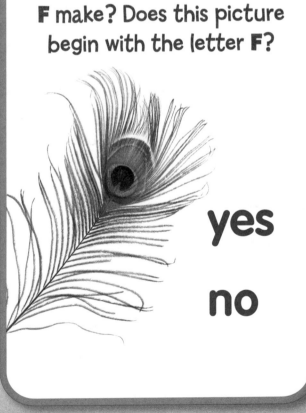

yes

no

Answers on page 277.

Circle the bunny in the hat.

Underline the words that begin with the letter **R**.

The race was really fun for each runner.

Circle the letter that is a vowel.

Z
U
X
J
P

Sing the song, then answer the question.

On Top of Spaghetti

♪ On top of spaghetti, ♫
All covered with cheese,
I lost my poor meatball,
When somebody sneezed.

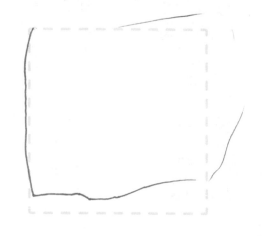

What was the spaghetti covered with?

pears   cheese   gum

Draw a square.

Answers on page 278.

Circle the one that is made from wool.

Circle the plate that has more cupcakes.

How many brown things do you see?

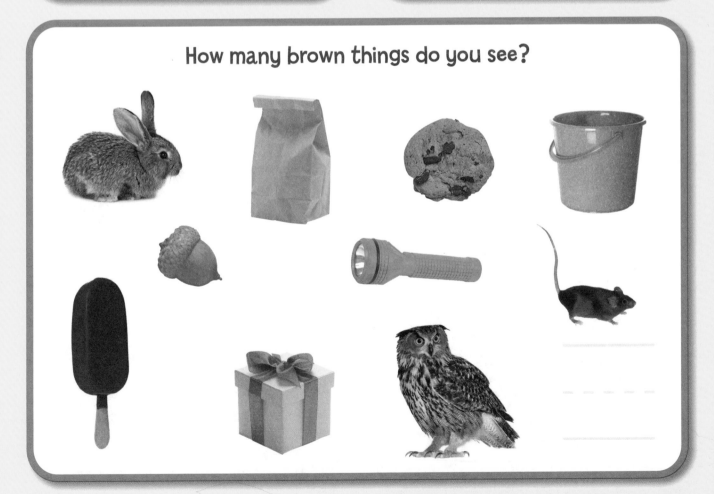

What is this?
Write its first letter.

Connect the two things that go together.

How many monkeys are jumping on the bed?

4

Put an X on the one that is different.

Answers on page 278.

Which animal belongs in this habitat?

Which one means hello in French?

bonjour   merci

Color the spaces that have the number 2.

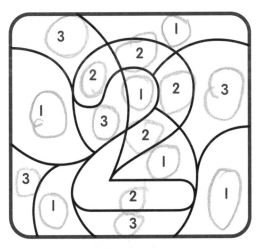

Draw a line under the one that is heavier.

Fill in the shapes to finish the pattern.

How many things in this picture start with the letter **T**?

Answers on page 279.

Circle the squirrel that collected the most acorns.

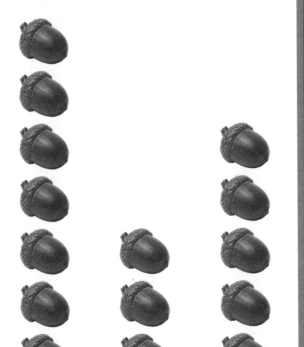

Circle the magazine.

Underline the words that begin with the letter **C**.

The coat in the closet has candy in its pockets.

Circle the one that is the opposite of left.

Is this temperature hot or cold?

hot

cold

How many shirts have dots?

Connect the two things that go together.

Circle the one that is full.

Answers on page 279.

Which would we wear in the summer?

Circle the things that begin with the letter D.

Underline the words that begin with the letter M.

My mother makes muffins on Mondays.

Circle the plant that is the youngest.

Circle the letter that is a vowel.

I

N

Q

C

H

Circle the things that begin with the letter **B**.

Find and circle 4 letter **P**s in this picture.

Answers on page 280.

Draw a line under the one that is lighter.

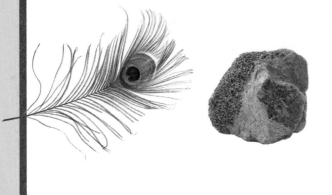

Circle the book.

How many ice pops are there?

Which animal is found in this habitat?

Draw a line under the one that travels in the air.

Answers on page 280.

Circle the letter that is a vowel.

M

P

O

W

K

Circle the things that begin with the letter C.

Underline the words that begin with the letter H.

He was hunting for honey on the hillside.

Circle the one you use to cut food.

Circle the xylophone.

94

Answers on page 280.

Which person is the tallest?

Connect the two things that go together.

Which animal belongs in this habitat?

Answers on page 280.

What sound does the letter **B** make? Does this picture begin with the letter **B**?

yes   **no**

Circle the one that begins with the letter **O**.

Which person do you see when you're sick?

What is this? Write its first letter.

Answers on page 281.

How many blue things do you see?

Where does the President of the United States live?

Find and circle 4 letter Ws in the picture.

Which animal belongs in this habitat?

How many birds are there?

Draw a line to cut the apple in half.

Put an X on the vase that has fewer flowers.

Trace the word.

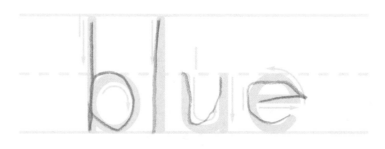

blue

Answers on page 281.

Circle the one that finishes the pattern.

Trace the word, then color the picture.

Circle the person who is taller.

What sound does the letter K make? Does this picture begin with the letter K?

yes   no

Draw a line under the rock that is smooth.

Circle the letter that is a vowel.

P

B

E

C

R

Sing the song, then answer the question.

Buckle My Shoe

One, two, buckle my shoe;
Three, four, shut the door;
Five, six, pick up sticks;
Seven, eight, lay them straight;
Nine, ten, do it again!

What do you pick up after five and six?

shoes hats sticks

Draw a line under the puppy in the middle.

Circle the seatbelt.

Circle the leaf.

Circle the ballet shoes.

How many chairs are there?

Draw a line under the one that is heavier.

Fill in the shapes to finish the pattern.

Color the spaces that have the number **1**.

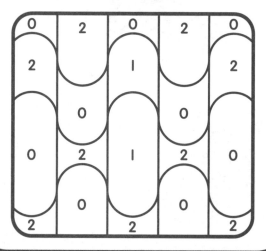

Which animal belongs in this habitat?

Circle the one that is empty.

Put an **X** on the one that is different.

Which holiday are these children celebrating?

Halloween

Answers on page 282.

Are there more ducks or ducklings? Circle the answer.

ducks   ducklings

What is this?
Write its first letter.

_____

What sound does the letter **N** make? Does this picture begin with the letter **N**?

yes   no

Connect the two things that go together.

Underline the words that begin with the letter **L**.

Let's lounge on the lawn after lunch.

Draw a line under the one that is lighter.

Which one means **stop**?

Draw a diamond.

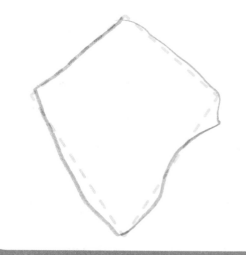

Put an **X** on the basket that has fewer strawberries.

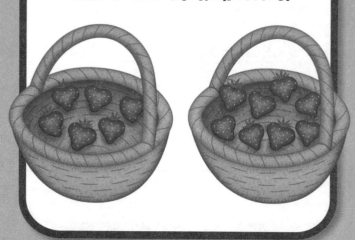

Circle the letter that is a vowel.

A
V
F
B
N

Answers on page 283.

What is this?
Write its first letter.

Circle the one that begins
with the letter C.

Circle the things that begin with the letter L.

Answers on page 283.

What sound does the letter **C** make? Does this picture begin with the letter **C**?

yes

no

Circle the helmet.

What is this?
Write its first letter.

Circle the group that has more.

Answers on page 283.

Circle the fishbowl that has more fish.

Connect the two things that go together.

Circle the letters that are consonants.

I   V
  A
M   T

Circle the one that is colder.

Underline the words that begin with the letter **N**.

Nick never found the note that Nancy sent.

How many balloons are there?

What is the girl celebrating?

birthday

Circle the things that begin with the letter **H**.

108

Answers on page 284.

What sound does the letter **L** make? Does this picture begin with the letter **L**?

yes   no

Find and circle the word **go** in the picture.

Circle the one that finishes the pattern.

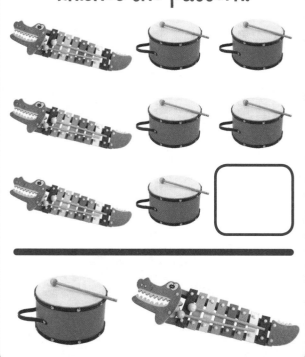

Circle the roots.

Answers on page 284.

Circle the group that has more.

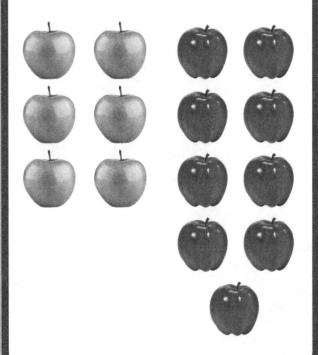

What sound does the letter **M** make? Does this picture begin with the letter **M**?

yes

no

What is this? Write its first letter.

_ _ _ _ _ _ _

_ _ _ _ _ _ _

Circle the one that begins with the letter **E**.

Answers on page 284.

Which person is older?

Which animal belongs in this habitat?

Which one means **thank you** in French?

au revoir　　merci

Color the spaces that have the number **4**.

	3		3			1
1	4		4	2		3
2		3	2		4	1	2
3	4		4	3		4
2		4		2	3	1
1				1	4
2	1	4	3	4	1	2
	3	2			2

Fill in the shapes to finish the pattern.

Trace the word.

green

Draw a line under the one that travels on the road.

Connect the ones that are the same.

What sound does the letter **J** make? Does this picture begin with the letter **J**?

yes   no

112

Answers on page 285.

Underline the words that begin with the letter **G**.

My grandma gives the best gifts!

Circle the one you use to eat soup.

Circle the letters that are consonants.

O D
U
X B

Are there more pumpkins or oranges? Circle the answer.

pumpkins

oranges

Draw a circle.

Which one flies to the moon?

Who takes care of barnyard animals?

Which one means excuse me in French?

pardon   **de rien**

Circle the group that has more.

How many chicks are there?

Answers on page 285.

How many diamonds are there?

Which animal belongs in this habitat?

Find and circle the letter **D** in this picture.

Trace the word, then color the picture.

top

Underline the words that begin with the letter **V**.

Vivian's voice was very pretty with the violin.

Put an **X** on the group that has fewer pencils.

Draw a line to cut the orange in half.

Draw a line under the rock that is rough.

Circle the letter that is a vowel.

K   F

D

G   O

Answers on page 286.

Put an **X** on the animal that is not an insect.

Circle the one that finishes the pattern.

Color the spaces that have the number **3**.

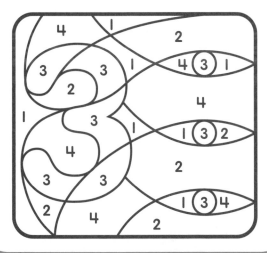

What meal do you eat before lunch?

dinner   breakfast

Fill in the shapes to finish the pattern.

Answers on page 286.

What color bead comes next? Circle the answer.

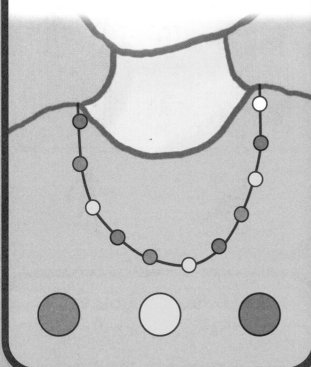

How many rectangles do you see in the house?

Connect the two things that go together.

Circle the one that begins with the letter P.

Answers on page 286.

Find and circle 7 letter **Z**s in this picture.

How many of these foods are fruits?

Circle the letter that is a vowel.

E

Q

D

T

V

Circle the body part you use to smell.

Underline the words that begin with the letter **D**.

The December school dance will be during the day.

Trace the word, then color the picture.

pig

Draw a line under the easel.

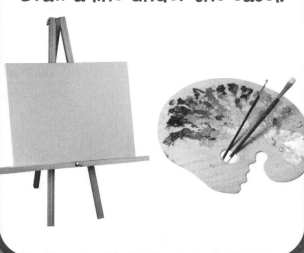

Answers on page 287.

Circle the one that is floating.

Circle the plate that has more cookies.

Circle the one that begins with the letter I.

Write the first letter of this word.

og

Circle the one that matches the fruits in the square.

Circle the Earth.

Who lives in the tepee?

Circle the one that is the opposite of short.

Answers on page 287.

Circle the one that finishes the pattern.

Which person is the shortest?

Which one would we wear in the snow?

What sound does the letter **T** make? Does this picture begin with the letter **T**?

yes   no

Answers on page 287.

What sound does the letter **X** make? Does this picture begin with the letter **X**?

yes   **no**

Connect the two things that go together.

What is this? Write its first letter.

_____

— — — — — — —

_____

Where do we buy food?

124

Which animal belongs in this habitat?

Find and circle the word bus in this picture.

Put an X on the one that is different.

What is the cat wearing?

hat

shoe

How many strawberries are there?

Circle the letters that are consonants.

G R A O E

Draw a star.

Underline the word that begins with the letter **X**.

Suzie needs an X-ray of her arm.

Sing the song, then answer the question.

Where Is Thumbkin?

Where is Thumbkin?
Where is Thumbkin?
Here I am!
Here I am!
How are you this morning?
Very well, I thank you.
Run away.
Run away.

Which finger is Thumbkin?

thumb   pinky

Circle the stem of the plant.

Answers on page 288.

Circle the one that begins with the letter S.

What color button comes next? Circle the answer.

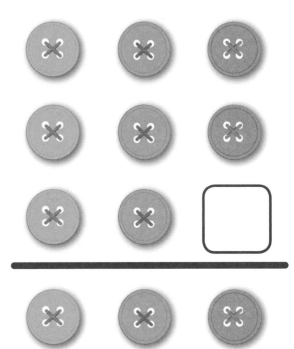

Are there more gorillas or goats? Circle the answer.

gorillas   goats

Write the first letter of this word.

ift

Answers on page 288.

Trace the word, then color the picture.

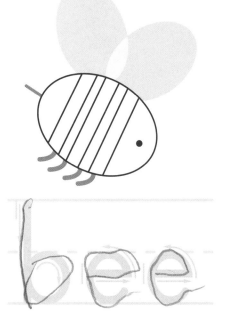

bee

Which one means **good night** in French?

bonne nuit   **bonjour**

Circle the one that matches the animal in the square.

What sound does the letter **P** make? Does this picture begin with the letter **P**?

yes   no

Answers on page 289.

Find and circle the word **up** in this picture.

Are these shapes all squares?

yes   no

Find and circle the letter **T** in this picture.

Color the spaces that have the number **7**.

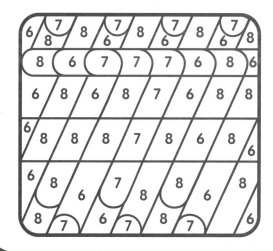

Fill in the shapes to finish the pattern.

Circle the tap shoes.

What is the duck riding?

truck   bike

How many sides does a triangle have? Write the number.

Circle the one that is hotter.

Which holiday is this girl celebrating?

Valentine's Day

Answers on page 289.

Trace the word, then color the picture.

sun

Connect the ones that are the same.

Circle the group that has more.

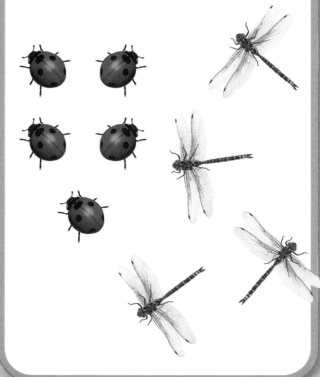

What is this? Write its first letter.

Circle the group that has more.

What sound does the letter **R** make? Does this picture begin with the letter **R**?

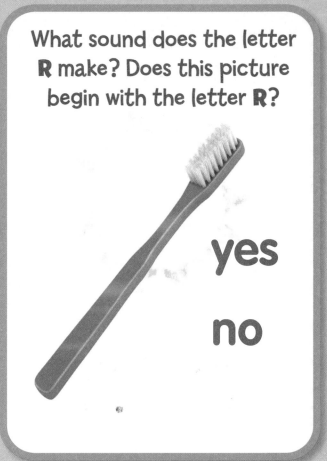

yes

no

Circle the one that begins with the letter **W**.

Circle the piano.

Answers on page 290.

Circle the letter that is a vowel.

J G
S
I R

Underline the words that begin with the letter **F**.

The family watches fireworks while they fish.

Circle the instrument students played most.

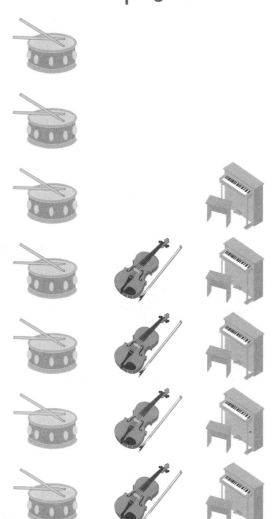

Circle the body part you use to touch.

Draw a line to cut the square in half.

Answers on page 290.

Which animal belongs in this habitat?

Which one of these planets is the biggest?

Earth   Jupiter   Saturn

Answers on page 290.

Trace the word, then color the picture.

owl

Connect the ones that are the same.

Which person prepares food?

What is this? Write its first letter.

Are these shapes all hearts?

yes   **no**

Find and circle the word **ice** in this picture.

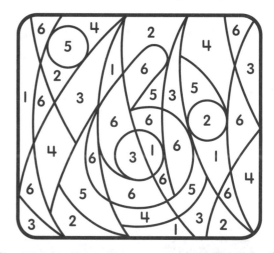

Circle the tree that has more apples.

Color the spaces that have the number **6**.

Trace the word.

black

136

Answers on page 291.

What is this?
Write its first letter.

_____

_____

Find and circle 4 letter Ks in this picture.

Connect the ones that are the same.

What sound does the letter H make? Does this picture begin with the letter H?

yes

no

Answers on page 291.

Circle the one that matches the fruit in the square.

What sound does the letter **y** make? Does this picture begin with the letter **y**?

yes   **no**

Write the first letter of this word.

_ig

Chart each item below.

	1	2	3	4	5
🏈					
⚽					

Answers on page 291.

Which child is not following the rules?

How many goldfish are there?

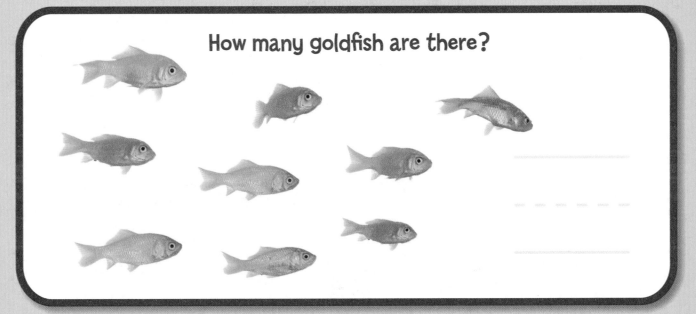

Circle the one that's exactly the same as the one in the circle.

Answers on page 291.

Draw a line under the one that travels on tracks.

Fill in the shapes to finish the pattern.

Which person keeps you and your neighborhood safe?

What is this? Write its first letter.

140

Answers on page 292.

Circle the letters that are consonants.

A

P

O

K

F

Circle the one that is full.

Sing the song, then answer the question.

Yankee Doodle

Yankee Doodle went to town,
Riding on a pony.
He stuck a feather in his cap,
And called it macaroni.

What did Yankee Doodle stick a feather in?

pony   town   cap

Underline the words that begin with the letter **J**.

In January, Joyce wears a jeweled jacket.

Draw a line under the one that is heavier.

Find and circle 3 letter **B**s in this picture.

Circle the one that finishes the pattern.

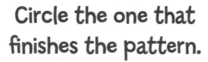
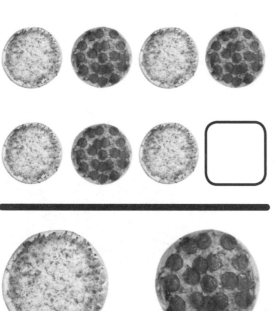

Which one would a baker wear?

142

Answers on page 292.

Connect the two things that go together.

SANTA CLAUS
123 CANDY CANE LANE
NORTH POLE

What sound does the letter **V** make? Does this picture begin with the letter **V**?

yes

no

Which person is younger?

What is this? Write its first letter.

Circle the knee pads.

Uh-oh! Hippo knocked the plant over. What should he say?

Thank you.

I'm sorry.

Circle the letters that are consonants.

T P I E K

Underline the words that begin with the letter **T**.

The track team practiced for two hours.

Answers on page 293.

Are there more orange or pink dinosaurs? Circle the answer.

orange   **pink**

Is this temperature hot or cold?

hot

cold

Write the first letter of this word.

ite

Which person helps you find books?

What sound does the letter **G** make? Does this picture begin with the letter **G**?

yes

no

Put an **X** on the one that is different.

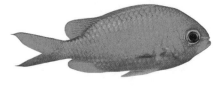

Are there more purple or green crayons? Circle the answer.

purple　　**green**

What is this? Write its first letter.

Answers on page 293.

Which one means **yes** in French?

oui   merci

Find and circle the letter **z** in the soup.

Are these shapes all diamonds?

yes   no

What's sitting on the dog?

dog   frog

Fill in the shapes to finish the pattern.

Find and circle the word **stop** in this picture.

Trace the word, then color the picture.

Write the first letter of this word.

Circle the one that matches the robot in the square.

Answers on page 294.

How many sides does
a diamond have?
Write the number.

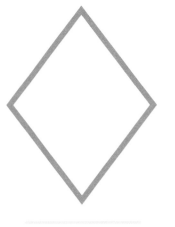

Which person helps you
cross the street?

Which animal belongs in this habitat?

Circle the one that finishes the pattern.

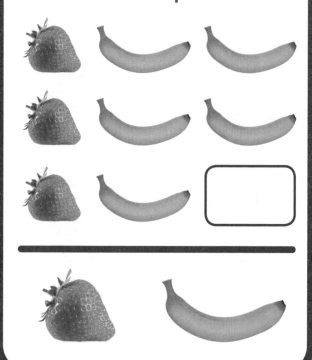

What is this? Write its first letter.

What sound does the letter **W** make? Does this picture begin with the letter **W**?

yes   no

Put an **X** on the one that is different.

150

Answers on page 294.

Circle the ones that begin with the letter **V**.

Circle the group that has more.

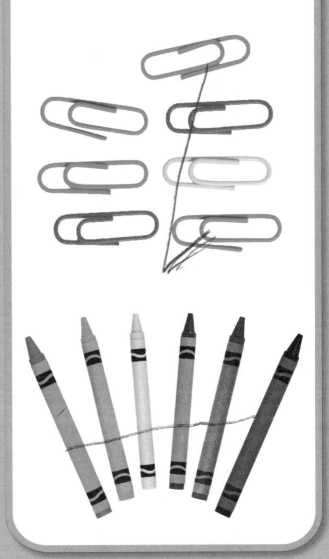

Circle the bag that is full.

Underline the words that begin with the letter **y**.

Your friend yodeled in my yard yesterday.

Find and circle 7 letter **C**s in this picture.

Can you name each of the 7 objects?

Which person helps at a restaurant?

Which one goes with the toothbrush?

Answers on page 295.

What is the boy wearing on his head?

ring

crown

Write the first letter of this word.

ree

How many squares are there?

Put an **X** on the one that is different.

Answers on page 295.

Draw a line under the person who is first in line.

Circle the plant that is older.

Underline the words that begin with the letter **K**.

The kettle in the kitchen is kept on the stove.

Circle the letters that are consonants.

E

B

Q O D

Circle the one you see at night.

Put an **X** on the one that is different.

Circle the one that begins with the letter **K**.

Circle the one that matches the car in the square.

What is this? Write its first letter.

Answers on page 295.

What sound does the letter Q make? Does this picture begin with the letter Q?

yes

no

Circle the one that is the opposite of big.

Circle the drums.

Write the first letter of this word.

ish

Answers on page 296.

Trace the word.

red

Sing the song, then answer the question.

Old MacDonald

Old MacDonald had a farm,
E, I, E, I, O.
And on this farm he had a
pig, E, I, E, I, O.
With an oink-oink here and
an oink-oink there,
Here an oink, there an oink,
everywhere an oink-oink.
Old MacDonald had a farm,
E, I, E, I, O.

What did Old MacDonald have?

a farm   a factory   a school

Match the coat to the right body part.

Find and circle the word **on**.

How many sides does a square have? Write the number.

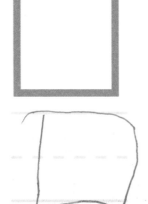

Put an **X** on the one that is different.

Draw a line under the one that travels on water.

Answers on page 296.

What is this?
Write its first letter.

Put an **X** on the one that is different.

Connect the ones that are the same.

Trace the word, then color the picture.

bus

Circle the letter that is a vowel.

U

R

D

B

S

Which box is closed?

Which ball is bigger?

Sing the song, then answer the question.

Make New Friends

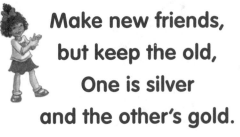

Make new friends,
but keep the old,
One is silver
and the other's gold.
A circle's round,
it has no end,
That's how long
you will be my friend.

Which star is gold?

Underline the words that begin with the letter **P**.

The pink pansy plant costs a pretty penny.

Answers on page 297.

Color the spaces that have the number 9.

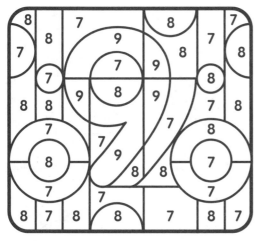

Put an X on the stand that has fewer cupcakes.

Draw a line under the one that is heavier.

Circle the one that is the opposite of up.

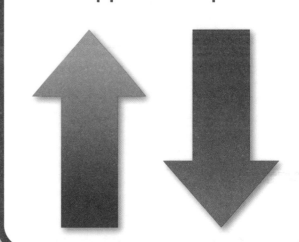

Fill in the shapes to finish the pattern.

Are these shapes all circles?

yes   **no**

Circle the one that is colder.

Circle the body part you use to see.

Circle the one that matches the ball in the square.

Trace the word.

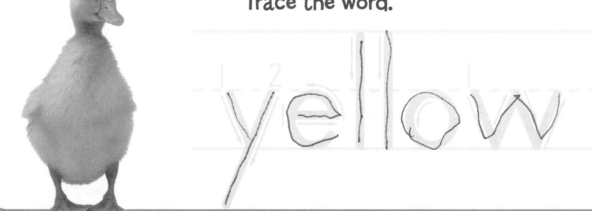

yellow

Answers on page 297.

Connect the two things that go together.

What is this? Write its first letter.

Find and circle 5 letter Ss in this picture.

Which person cleans your teeth?

Answers on page 297.

Draw a line to cut the cake in half.

Which one will stick to the magnet?

Underline the words that begin with the letter **W**.

Willy was a wonderful worker every Wednesday.

Circle the car that faces front.

Circle the letters that are consonants.

P   I
U
X   L

Answers on page 298.

Which person is in the army?

What is this?
Write its first letter.

Circle the ice cream that was ordered the most.

Answers on page 298.

Write the first letter of this word.

tar

Circle the one that finishes the pattern.

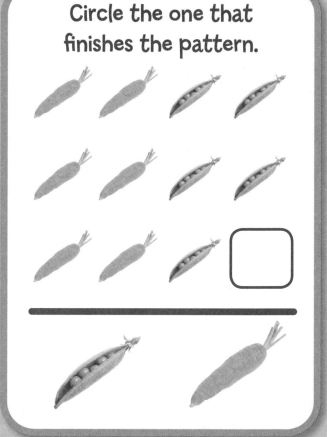

Which one means **good-bye** in French?

au revoir   oui

What is this? Write its first letter.

166

Answers on page 298.

Sing the song, then answer the question.

The Ants Go Marching

The ants go marching one by one, hurrah, hurrah!
The ants go marching one by one, hurrah, hurrah!
The ants go marching one by one,
The little one stops to suck his thumb,
And they all go marching down to the ground
To get out of the rain, BOOM! BOOM! BOOM!

What were the ants trying to get out of?

work   **the rain**   **trouble**

Which team won the game?

How many leaves are there?

Which animal belongs in this habitat?

168

Answers on page 299.

Find and circle 5 letter Xs in this picture.

**What is this?
Write its first letter.**

What sound does the letter Z make? Does this picture begin with the letter Z?

yes   no

Where do we go if we are sick?

Circle the one that begins with the letter **L**.

Put an **X** on the one that is different.

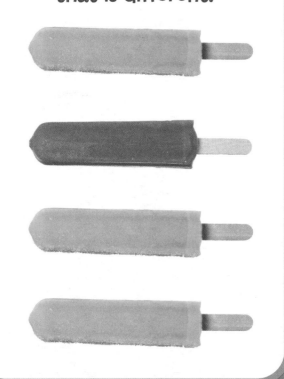

Trace the word, then color the picture.

fox

Find and circle the word **no**.

NO PARKING ANY TIME

Answers on page 299.

Color the spaces that have the number 8.

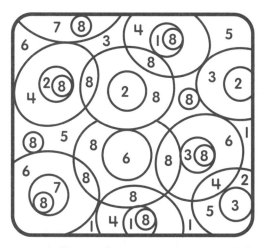

Circle the one that is hotter.

Put an X on the tree that has fewer leaves.

What is the bear holding?

pear apple

Which holiday is this boy celebrating?

Thanksgiving

Circle the newspaper.

Which one would we wear in the rain?

Circle the one that finishes the pattern.

What is this?
Write its first letter.

172

Answers on page 300.

Circle the one that is empty.

Circle the fruit that was picked most.

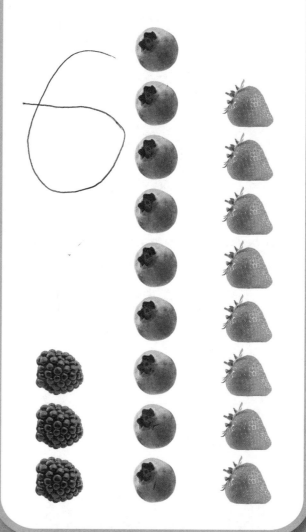

Underline the words that begin with the letter **Q**.

Quickly tell the queen that the quest is over!

Circle the one you use to eat a salad.

Circle the letters that are consonants.

O   A
  E
P   Z

Match the hat to the right body part.

Circle the one that is colder.

Put an **X** on the one that is different.

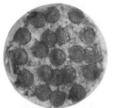

Are these shapes all stars?

yes   no

Which of these is a musical instrument?

174

Answers on page 300.

Connect the two things that go together.

How many yellow stars are in the sky?

What is this?
Write its first letter.

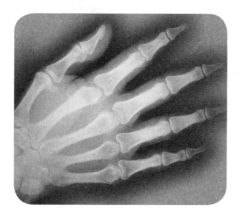

What sound does the letter **S** make? Does this picture begin with the letter **S**?

yes   no

Answers on page 300.

Find and circle 6 letter Fs in this picture.

Circle the one that begins with the letter T.

What is this? Write its first letter.

Which person helps sick animals?

Answers on page 301.

Circle the one that's exactly the same as the top crayon.

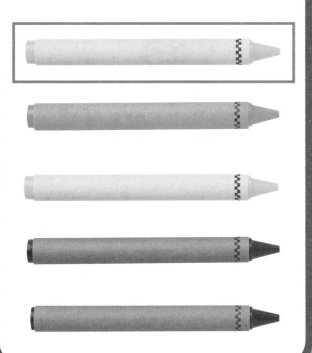

Put an **X** on the one that will not stick to the magnet.

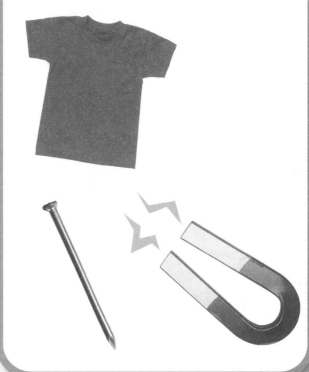

Which animal belongs in this habitat?

Answers on page 301.

Circle the letters that are consonants.

U
I E
M N

What animal is in the boat?

cat   goat

Draw a line under the person who is last in line.

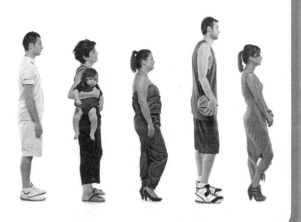

Color the spaces that have the number **10**.

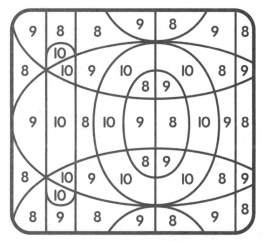

9	8	8	9	8	9	8
10						
8	10	9	10	10	8	9
			8	9		
9	10	8	10	9	8	10	9	8
			8	9		
8	10	9	10	10	8	9
10						
8	9	8	9	8	9	8

Which holiday is this girl celebrating?

4th of July

Answers on page 301.

Which team lost the game?

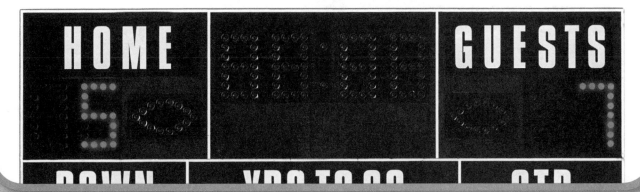

Fill in the shapes to finish the pattern.

What is this? Write its first letter.

Write the first letter of this word.

ar

Circle the letters that are consonants.

E

G

I

R

W

Circle the wrist guards.

Underline the words that begin with the letter **S**.

There are seven seashells on the sandy seashore.

Circle the ones that weigh less.

What is the meal that comes before dinner?

lunch   breakfast

Answers on page 302.

What is this?
Write its first letter.

_____

- - - - - - -

_____

Circle the one that finishes the pattern.

Which person helps fix roads?

Trace the word, then color the picture.

dog

Find and circle 2 letter Xs in the picture.

Connect the two things that go together.

Chart each item below.

	1	2	3	4	5
🥪		✓		✓	
🍔					

Circle the letter.

Answers on page 302.

Read the nursery rhyme, then answer the questions.

Little Miss Muffet

Little Miss Muffet
Sat on a tuffet,
Eating her curds and whey.
There came a big spider,
Who sat down beside her,
And frightened
Miss Muffet away.

What sat down beside
Little Miss Muffet?

What was Little Miss Muffet
sitting on?

Answers on page 302.

Trace the missing letter.
What is the word?

Circle the dog that is
inside the doghouse.

Circle the tomato.

Underline the words that
begin with the letter **Z**.

Zack saw
zero hippos
at the zoo.

Trace the missing letter.
What is the word?

184

Answers on page 303.

Match the sock to the right body part.

Circle the American flag.

What is the opposite of dark?

Circle the guitar.

Circle the things that begin with the letter **W**.

Which one of these planets is the smallest?

Venus   Saturn   Neptune

Circle the things that begin with the letter **G**.

How many hot dogs are there?

Answers on page 303.

Which word means **you're welcome** in French?

de rien   au revoir

Draw a line under the things you need to paint a picture.

Connect the two things that go together.

Find and circle the word **pet** in this picture.

Pet Shop

OPEN

Circle the things that begin with the letter **P**.

Connect the things that go together.

Circle the harmonica.

Answers on page 304.

Chart each item below.

	1	2	3	4	5
🛹					
🚲					

Circle the card.

What is the opposite of slow?

Match the mitten to the right body part.

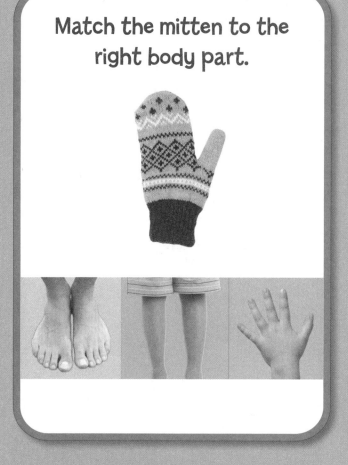

Trace the word.

purple

Circle the things that begin with the letter y.

Answers on page 304.

Find and circle the word **zoo** in this picture.

Connect the two things that go together.

How many flags have checkers?

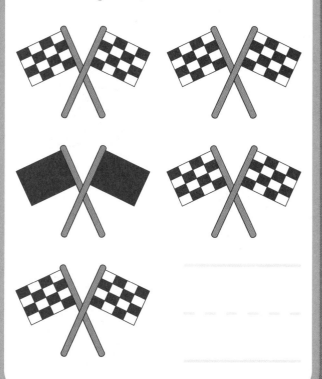

Which one is a vegetable?

Match the jeans to the right body part.

Connect the pictures that rhyme.

Find and circle 3 letter Rs in the picture.

Connect the things that go together.

192

Answers on page 305.

Trace the missing letter. What is the word?

p e t

Solve the addition problem.

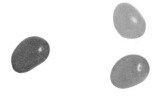

$1 + 2 =$

Which signal means walk?

Circle the things that begin with the letter F.

Trace the missing letter. What is the word?

10 t e n

Draw a line under the one that travels on snow.

Solve the addition problem.

Which one is the opposite of fast?

Connect the pictures that rhyme.

194

Answers on page 305.

Three Little Pigs

Once there were three
little pigs. The first built
a house of straw, and the
second built a house of sticks;
the third pig built a house of bricks.
One day a wolf came to all three
houses. He blew down the house
of straw and the house of
sticks! But when he tried
to blow the brick house
down, he couldn't.
The third pig had
outsmarted the wolf!

What did the second pig build his house with?

Which animal is feeling sick?

Trace the picture. What shape is it?

circle

oval

Solve the subtraction problem.

3 - 1 =

Circle the corn.

Draw a line under the sign that means a fire station is nearby.

Answers on page 306.

Which dog is the opposite of wet?

Which toy costs more?

Circle the monkey in the middle.

Connect the pictures that rhyme.

Answers on page 306.

Read the nursery rhyme, then answer the questions.

The Cat and the Fiddle

Hey, diddle, diddle,
The cat and the fiddle,
The cow jumped
Over the moon.
The little dog laughed
To see such sport,
And the dish ran away
With the spoon.

What did the cow jump over?

What instrument does the cat play?

Answers on page 306.

Circle the things that begin with the letter **U**.

Solve the addition problem.

 =

Match the word to the correct picture.

jar

Which children are skipping?

Answers on page 306.

Trace the missing letter. What is the word?

see

Circle the ballerina.

Solve the addition problem.

$$1 + 1 = \underline{}$$

Circle the paint can that is open.

Trace the missing letter. What is the word?

fin

Answers on page 307.

Number the events in the correct order.

Which sign tells you how to get out of a building?

Solve the subtraction problem.

$$4 - 2 = \underline{\qquad}$$

Trace the picture. What shape is it?

triangle

square

Circle the green beans.

How many pennies?

Fill in half of the circle.

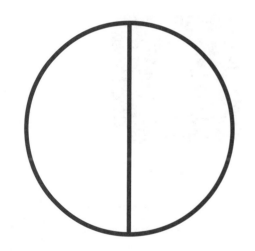

Match the word to the correct picture.

walrus

Answers on page 307.

Which one is the opposite of in?

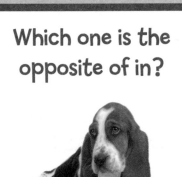

Which word means **head** in Spanish?

sol

cabeza

Connect the pictures that rhyme.

Connect the two things that go together.

Answers on page 307.

203

Connect the pictures that rhyme.

Which toy costs less?

Circle two things that help plants grow.

Circle the one that starts the same way as **egg**.

Answers on page 308.

Read the story, then answer the question.

Rapunzel

Once there was an evil witch who had a very tall tower. She kept Rapunzel locked up in the tower. Rapunzel had very long hair. One day, a handsome prince found Rapunzel and climbed up her hair to the tower. Then he helped her escape and they lived happily ever after.

Where did Rapunzel live?

Solve the addition problem.

Which one can you recycle?

Which one is the opposite of light?

Circle the one that starts the same way as **igloo**.

Answers on page 308.

Connect the pictures that rhyme.

Circle the bee that is under the flower.

What do you say when you politely ask for something?

please   **no**

What time is it?

3:00   **5:00**

Which fruit has two pieces that are the same?

Draw a line under the sign that means be careful.

Trace the missing letter. What is the word?

Solve the addition problem.

$$1 + 3 =$$

Answers on page 309.

Read the nursery rhyme, then answer the questions.

Little Bo Peep

Little Bo Peep
has lost her sheep,
And can't tell where
to find them.
Leave them alone,
And they'll come home,
Wagging their tails
behind them.

What did Little Bo Peep lose?

Circle the sheep's tail.

Answers on page 309.

Connect the pictures that rhyme.

Which one is the opposite of over?

What time is it?

3:00   **8:00**

Circle the person who is shorter.

Answers on page 309.

Circle the computer screen.

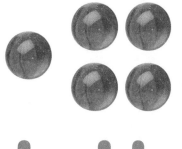

Solve the addition problem.

1 + 4 =

Circle the flag of Mexico.

Trace the picture. What shape is it?

triangle

square

Which one is a fruit?

Trace the missing letter. What is the word?

b i t

Which one tells you a train is nearby?

Solve the addition problem.

2 + 3 =

Fill in one fourth of the square.

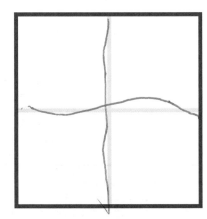

Trace the missing letter. What is the word?

s e w

Answers on page 310.

Solve the subtraction problem.

5 - 2 =

Match the word to the correct picture.

 **horse**

Which word means **hands** in Spanish?

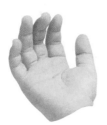

manos

ojos

Connect the pictures that rhyme.

What do you say when someone gives you a present?

thank you   sorry

Which one is the opposite of laugh?

Circle the one on the bottom.

Connect the pictures that rhyme.

Answers on page 310.

When plants start to grow, what season is it?

fall   spring

Match the word to the correct picture.

hat

Number the events in the correct order.

Answers on page 310.

Circle the toys that cost the same.

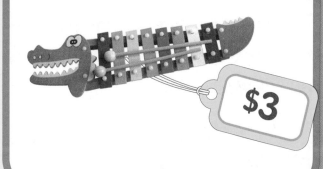

Draw a line under the sign that means boys' washroom.

Trace the missing letter. What is the word?

red

Trace the missing letter. What is the word?

sip

Answers on page 311.

Which one has three pieces that are the same?

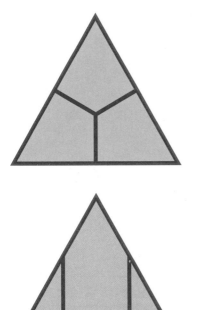

Connect the pictures that rhyme.

Match the goal to the right ball.

What is the mouse doing?

singing   talking

The Ugly Duckling

Once upon a time, a mother duck had some baby ducklings. All of the ducklings were little and yellow, except for one. He was big and gray. Everyone teased him and called him ugly.

When the ugly duckling grew up, he found out that he wasn't a duck at all! He was a swan. That was why he looked different from the other ducklings. He met other swans like him and they lived happily ever after.

What color was the ugly duckling?

gray   green   yellow

Answers on page 311.

Trace the missing letter. What is the word?

dig

Circle the mouse.

Solve the subtraction problem.

3 - 2 =

Circle the cauliflower.

Trace the missing letter. What is the word?

leg

Answers on page 311.

Which president is on the one dollar bill?

Connect the pictures that rhyme.

What time is it?

7:00   **9:00**

Which one is the opposite of sour?

220

Answers on page 312.

Circle the longer snake.

Trace the picture. What shape is it?

oval

star

How many dimes?

Match the word to the correct picture.

dinosaur

Draw a line under the sign that means a playground is nearby.

Answers on page 312.

Number the events in the correct order.

Which one is a fruit?

Solve the subtraction problem.

5 - 4 =

Answers on page 312.

Draw a line under the sign that means slippery floor.

Circle the toys that cost the same.

$10

$2

$2

Circle the onion.

Trace the missing letter. What is the word?

job

Trace the missing letter. What is the word?

Solve the subtraction problem.

$4-3=$

Circle the broccoli.

Draw a line under the sign that means recycle.

Trace the missing letter. What is the word?

net

Answers on page 313.

Connect the pictures
that rhyme.

Circle the one that starts
the same way as **bat**.

Circle the gifts on the left.

Which word means
water in Spanish?

agua

leche

Number the events in the correct order.

_____   _____

_____   _____

_____   _____

Which food grows under the ground?

Which one is the opposite of old?

Trace the picture. What shape is it?

diamond

star

Solve the addition problem.

 **+**    **=** _____

Answers on page 313.

Circle the plane that is above the cloud.

Connect the pictures that rhyme.

Circle the one that starts the same way as **door**.

Circle the keyboard.

Match the goal to the right ball.

Which of these grows on a tree?

How many quarters?

Circle the bin you would use to recycle this bottle.

Answers on page 314.

Read the nursery rhyme, then answer the question.

Little Boy Blue

Little Boy Blue,
Come blow your horn.
The sheep's in the meadow,
The cow's in the corn.

Where's the little boy
Who looks after the sheep?
Under the haystack
Fast asleep.

Where was Little Boy Blue sleeping?

Connect the pictures that rhyme.

Which toy costs less?

$9

$10

Which one should you use to wipe your nose?

Circle the one that starts the same way as **jack**.

230

Answers on page 314.

Trace the missing letter. What is the word?

a r m

Circle the chopsticks.

Solve the subtraction problem.

5 - 1 =

Trace the missing letter. What is the word?

b u g

Circle the lettuce.

Match the word to the correct picture.

boat

Which one can you recycle?

Circle the flag of Canada.

What should you do when you cough?

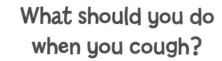

Which one is a fruit?

Answers on page 315.

Match the ball to the right equipment.

Which toy costs more?

$8

$10

Circle the one that starts the same way as **uncle**.

Which one is the opposite of glad?

Answers on page 315.

Read the nursery rhyme, then answer the questions.

Humpty Dumpty

Humpty Dumpty sat on a wall;
Humpty Dumpty had a great fall!
All the king's horses
And all the king's men
Couldn't put Humpty
together again.

What did Humpty Dumpty fall from?

Did Humpty Dumpty get put back together again?

yes

no

Answers on page 315.

Match the word to the correct picture.

star

Connect the pictures that rhyme.

Which one is the opposite of clean?

What instrument is the girl playing?

guitar   **violin**

Answers on page 315.

Match the word to the correct picture.

truck

Circle the one that starts the same way as **nut**.

Which one is the opposite of small?

Match the ball to the right equipment.

Answers on page 316.

What numbers would you dial in an emergency?

Which toy costs more?

$9

$5

Number the events in the correct order.

Which one is the opposite of float?

Connect the pictures that rhyme.

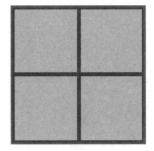

Connect the pictures that rhyme.

Which one has four pieces that are the same?

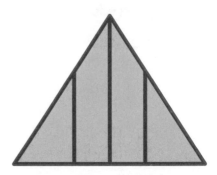

Answers on page 316.

Circle the one that starts the same way as **rock**.

Draw a line under the sign that means girls' washroom.

Trace the missing letter. What is the word?

f ar

Circle the tallest building.

Which one is a vegetable?

Circle the group of coins that is equal to the exact price.

Draw a line under the sign that means there is a crosswalk nearby.

240

Answers on page 317.

Which word means **feet** in Spanish?

pies

regalos

What time is it?

1:00   5:00

Circle the animal who is upside-down.

Connect the pictures that rhyme.

Snow White

There once was a wicked queen with a magic mirror. It said that Snow White was more beautiful than the queen. Snow White was scared, so she ran into the forest, where she found seven dwarfs living in a cottage. One day, the queen tried to poison Snow White. But a prince saved her and they lived happily ever after.

How many dwarfs did Snow White find in the forest?

5   6   7

Answers on page 317.

How many nickels?

Trace the missing letter. What is the word?

hop

Which food grows above the ground?

Which word means **kitchen** in Spanish?

cuarto de baño

cocina

Solve the subtraction problem.

5 - 1 =

Answers on page 317.

Find and circle the word **home** in this picture.

Solve the addition problem.

Connect the pictures that rhyme.

Match the word to the correct picture.

frog

244

Answers on page 318.

Which signal means don't walk?

Circle the items that cost the same.

$1

$1

$6

Solve the subtraction problem.

4-3=

Trace the missing letter. What is the word?

dip

Which sign tells you a hospital is nearby?

Solve the addition problem.

 +    = _____

Which one can you recycle?

Answers on page 318.

Which person is jumping the rope?

Match the word to the correct picture.

sun

Connect the pictures that rhyme.

Which toy bear costs less?

$9

$7

Read the nursery rhyme, then answer the questions.

Pease Porridge Hot

Pease porridge hot,
Pease porridge cold,
Pease porridge in the pot,
Nine days old.
Some like it hot,
Some like it cold,
Some like it in the pot,
Nine days old.

How many days old
is the porridge?

2   5   9

Where is the porridge?

248

Answers on page 319.

Connect the pictures that rhyme.

Match the word to the correct picture.

lamb

Number the events in the correct order.

1   2   3

Which one is a vegetable?

Solve the subtraction problem.

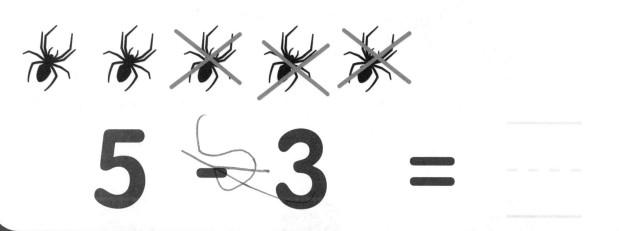

5 - 3 =

Draw a line under the sign that means bicycle crossing.

Answers on page 319.

Circle the smaller cat.

What time is it?

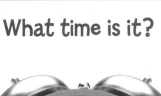

2:00   **9:00**

Connect the pictures that rhyme.

Match the ball to the right equipment.

Answers on page 319.

Number the events in the correct order.

Connect the pictures that rhyme.

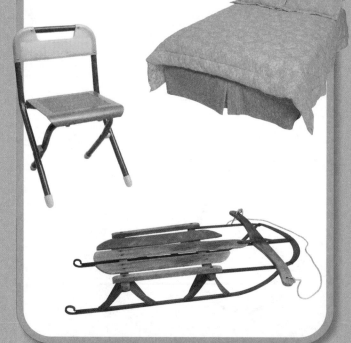

Which toy costs more?

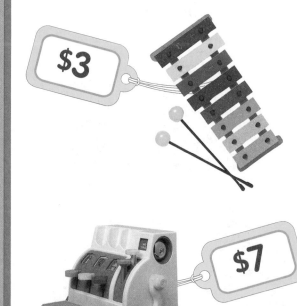

$3

$7

Answers on page 320.

Goldilocks and the Three Bears

One day, a little girl named Goldilocks found an empty house that belonged to three bears. She ate their porridge and fell asleep in Baby Bear's bed. The three bears came home and saw that their porridge had been eaten, and that Goldilocks was

asleep. Goldilocks woke up, saw the bears, and ran away as fast as she could!

Where did Goldilocks fall asleep?

Trace the missing letter. What is the word?

hug

Which one is a star?

Solve the addition problem.

3+2=

Circle the peppers.

Trace the missing letter. What is the word?

win

Answers on page 320.

Which bird is the symbol of America?

Circle the group of coins that is equal to the exact price.

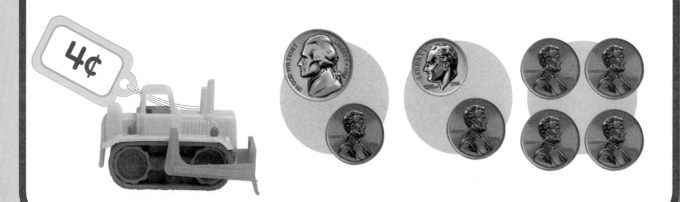

Circle the letters **S, M, A, R**, and **T** on this keyboard. What do they spell?

Answers on page 320.

CONGRATULATIONS!

You have made it to the end of a very big workbook! That's something to be proud of!

You've learned about...

 Letters & words

 Numbers & counting

 Adding & subtracting

✔ Shapes   ✔ Animals

✔ Colors   ✔ People

✔ Plants   ✔ Planets

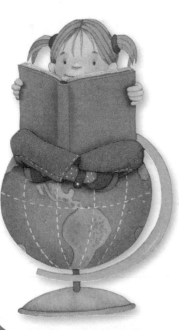

Super Smart

_____

Name

_____

Date

Answers

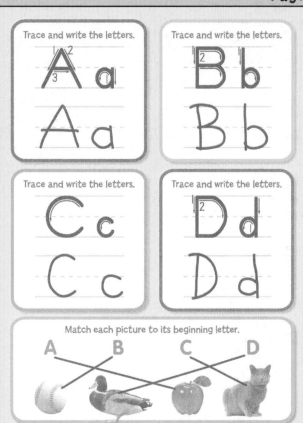

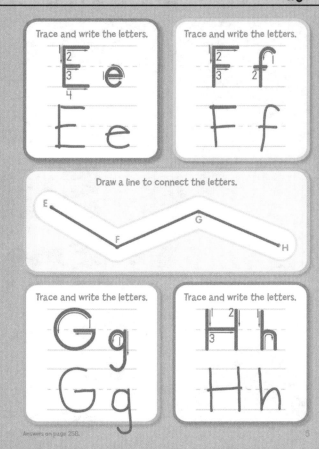

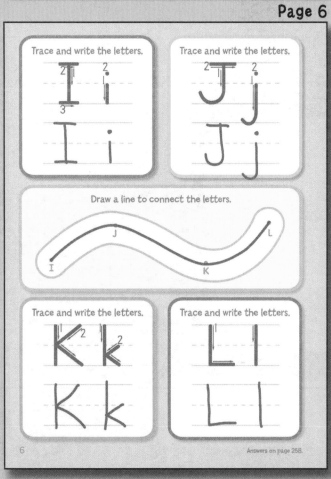

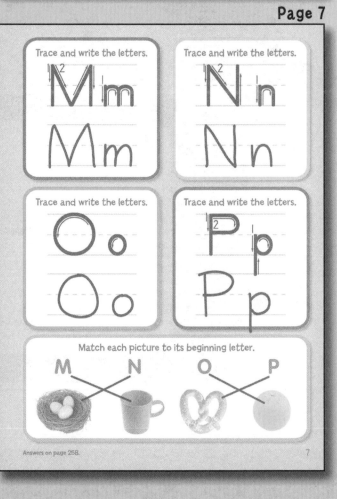

Page 8

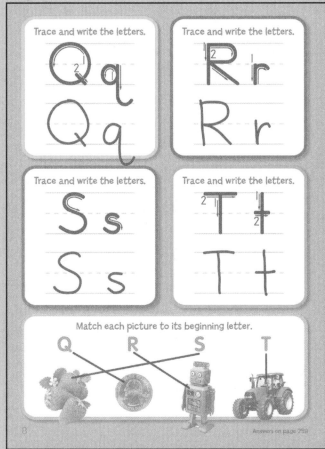

Page 9

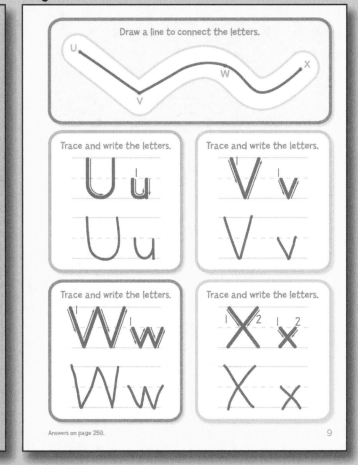

Page 10

Page 11

Answers

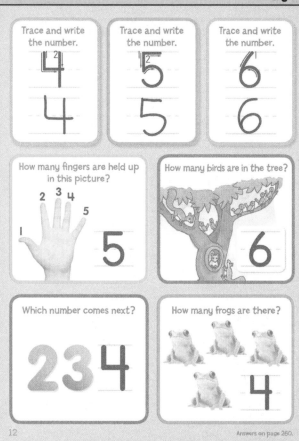

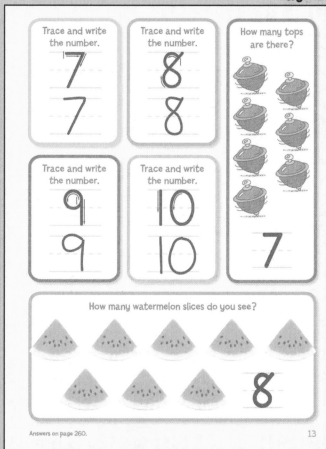

Answers on page 260.

Answers on page 260.

Answers on page 260.

Answers on page 260.

Page 16

How many fingers are held up in this picture?

1 2 3

3

Which person is wearing glasses?

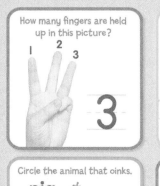

Circle the animal that oinks.

pig

Find and circle the word **hid**.

y h b a
d z k **h**
t b a **i**
o h c **d**

Fill in the missing number.

1 2 3 **4** 5 6

16

Answers on page 261.

Page 17

How many buttons can you find on the bear?

3

Is it hot or cold in this picture?

hot (**cold**)

Which letter comes next? Use the picture to help.

abc

Fill in the shapes that have the letter **F**. What is it?

flower

Answers on page 261.

17

Page 18

Follow the alphabet to connect the dots.

How many circles can you find?

8

Which letter comes next? Use the picture to help.

bcd

Connect the dots.

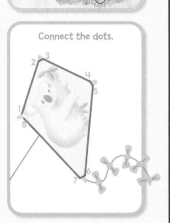

18

Answers on page 261.

Page 19

Circle the animal that meows.

cat

How many soccer balls? Circle the correct number.

1 2 (**3**) 4 5

How many fingers are held up in this picture?

1 2 3 4

4

What do you wash after using the bathroom?

(**hands**) face

Circle the creature that made this web.

spider

Answers on page 261.

19

Answers

Page 24

Circle the uppercase letters.

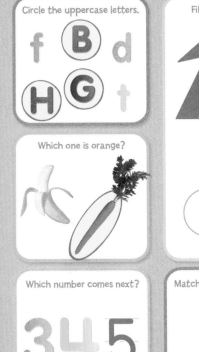

f **B** d

H **G** t

Fill in the triangles.

Which one is orange?

Which number comes next?

3 4 **5**

Match the food to its color.

yellow blue **red**

Answers on page 263.

24

Page 25

How many animals have spots?

2

How many bells are there?

5

Which letter comes next? Use the picture to help.

e f **g**

Answers on page 263.

25

Page 26

Circle the lowercase letters.

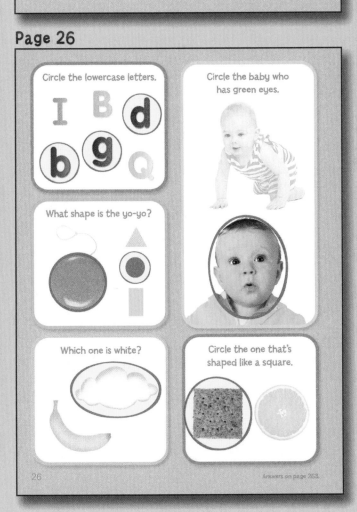

I B **d**

b **g** Q

What shape is the yo-yo?

Which one is white?

Circle the baby who has green eyes.

Circle the one that's shaped like a square.

Answers on page 263.

26

Page 27

Which letter comes next? Use the picture to help.

f g **h**

Is it windy or calm in this picture?

windy calm

Fill in the shapes that have the letter **W**. What is it?

whale

Which one means **hello** in Spanish?

adiós

hola

Answers on page 263.

27

Answers

Fill in the shapes that have the letter **S**. What is it?

star

Which letter comes next? Use the picture to help.

h i **j**

Connect the dots.

Put an **X** on each pair that does not have matching uppercase and lowercase letters.

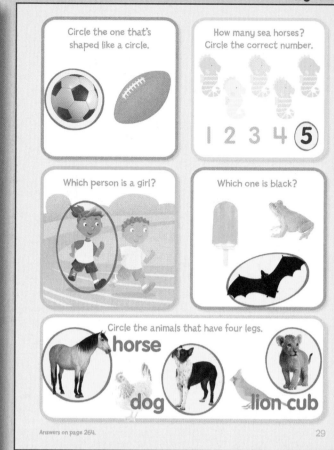

Circle the one that's shaped like a circle.

How many sea horses? Circle the correct number.

1 2 3 4 **5**

Which person is a girl?

Which one is black?

Circle the animals that have four legs.

horse   **dog**   **lion cub**

Match the food to its color.

green red **orange**

Find and circle the word **sun**.

u k y **s**
a c d **u**
e g h **n**
o b p d

Circle the uppercase letters.

f **Z** e **Q** **M** h

Which person is a boy?

Circle the animal that is a mammal.

dog

Who is sad?

Fill in the circles.

Which letter comes next? Use the picture to help.

i j **k**

Circle the pairs of matching uppercase and lowercase letters.

Dd   **Rr**   Qp   Nm

Answers

Page 32

Page 33

Page 34

Page 35

265

Answers

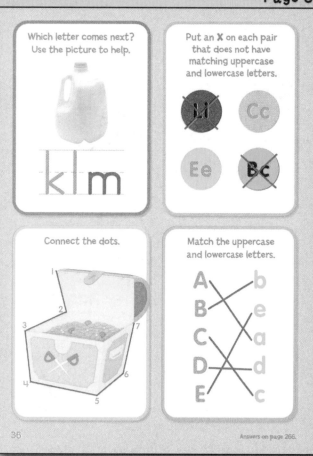

Page 40

How many fingers are held up in this picture?

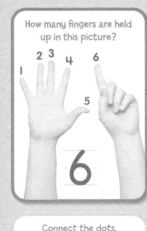

6

Which letter comes next? Use the picture to help.

l m n

Connect the dots.

Match the uppercase and lowercase letters.

P — r
Q — p
R — t
S — q
T — s

Answers on page 267.

Page 41

Which person has blond hair?

Which one is brown?

Which one is the sister?

Find and circle the word **win**.

w	d	e	h
i	c	t	a
n	u	z	g
p	v	k	w

Fill in the missing number.

2 3 4 5 6

Answers on page 267.

Page 42

How many green trucks do you see?

5

Which letter comes next? Use the picture to help.

n o p

Fill in the shapes that have the letter **B**. What is it?

butterfly

Which one means **good-bye** in Spanish?

hola

adiós

Answers on page 267.

Page 43

How many black things do you see?

3

Which letter comes next? Use the picture to help.

o p q

Follow the alphabet to connect the dots.

Answers on page 267.

Answers

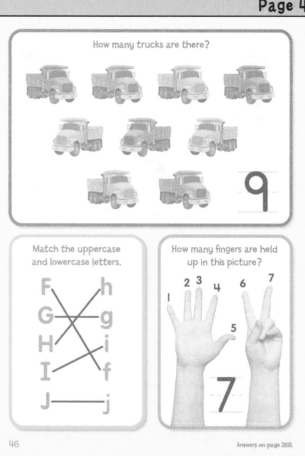

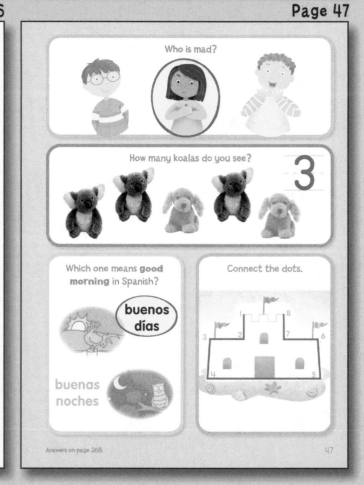

Page 48

Which person has black hair?

Find and circle the word **one**.

a n b c
w f i a
t v s h
o n e y

Which animal likes cheese?
mouse

Which one is the grandfather?

Circle the animal that neighs.

horse

Answers on page 269.

48

Page 49

Put an **X** on each pair that does not have matching uppercase and lowercase letters.

Hh   M̶n̶
Ww   X̶v̶

Follow the alphabet to connect the dots.

Circle the person who has brown eyes.

How many apples are in the tree?

5

Answers on page 269.

49

Page 50

Circle the lowercase letters.

j d P
D e T

Match the uppercase and lowercase letters.

U — w
V — u
W — y
X — v
Y — z
Z — x

Circle the body part you eat with.
mouth

Match the food to its color.

green   orange   **blue**

Which number comes next?
5 6 7

Answers on page 269.

50

Page 51

What do we say if we hurt someone's feelings?

sorry   thank you

Which letter comes next? Use the picture to help.

q r s

Put an **X** on each pair that does not have matching uppercase and lowercase letters.

Xx   Y̶z̶
V̶w̶   Uu

How many snowflakes? Circle the correct number.
6 ⑦ 8 9 10

Answers on page 269.

51

Answers

Which letter comes next? Use the picture to help.

r s t

Which one means **please** in Spanish?

el cerdo

por favor

Follow the alphabet to connect the dots.

Put an **X** on each pair that does not have matching uppercase and lowercase letters.

Vv   A p

C b   Ff

Answers on page 270.

Is it raining or snowing in this picture?

raining   snowing

Find and circle the word **pet**.

k h x z
p b d e
e q i t
t f m o

Which one is asleep?

cat

Which person is using crutches?

Fill in the missing number.

5   6   7   8   9

Is the bunny happy or angry?

happy   angry

Connect the dots.

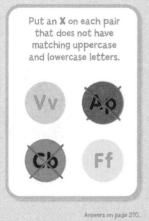

How many red wagons do you see?

3

Which letter comes next? Use the picture to help.

t u v

Answers on page 270.

Circle the one that's shaped like a diamond.

YIELD

Follow the alphabet to connect the dots.

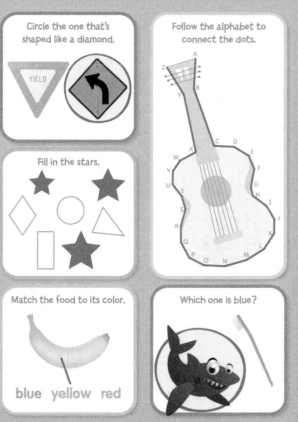

Fill in the stars.

Match the food to its color.

blue   yellow   red

Which one is blue?

Answers

Page 56

Circle the animal that has feathers.

chicken

Find and circle the word **bed**.

e b f d
j w v a
b e d c
k a s h

Which person wears braces?

Which animal is black and white?

Fill in the missing number.

5

3 4 ? 6 7

Answers on page 271.

Page 57

How many leaves? Circle the correct number.

6 7 8 **9** 10

Which letter comes next? Use the picture to help.

u v **w**

How many red things do you see?

7

Answers on page 271.

Page 58

Which one is the son?

Find and circle the word **two**.

d **t** h l
x **w** k p
y **o** f j
g c v b

Circle the imaginary animal.

unicorn

Match the food to its color.

green red orange

Which one is yellow?

What shape is the lollipop?

Answers on page 271.

Page 59

Which number comes next?

6 7 **8**

Follow the alphabet to connect the dots.

Fill in the diamonds.

Match the food to its color.

black yellow red

Circle the lowercase letters.

n I **g**
N O K

Answers on page 271.

Answers

Circle the one that's shaped like a star.

What should we say when we see someone?

(hello)
good-bye

Match the food to its color.

green red (white)

Which number comes next?

7 8 9

Find and circle the word **mitt**.

o e d z
l j a o
(m i t t)
s c k e

Answers on page 272.

Which person has a cast?

What two shapes make this ice-cream cone?

Which one do you use to comb your hair?

comb

Which one is the brother?

Which food should the rabbit eat?

carrot

Answers on page 272.

How many orange things do you see?

3

Which letter comes next? Use the picture to help.

V W X

Connect the dots.

Answers on page 272.

Which one is the daughter?

Which one is red?

Find and circle the word **job**.

z p w h
b y a c
e d v e
(j o b) l

What shape is the door?

Circle the animal that trumpets.

elephant

Circle the lowercase letters.

(q) R (U) G W (a)

Answers on page 272.

272

Answers

Page 64

Match the uppercase and lowercase letters.

K — m
L — k
M — n
N — o
O — l

Which one means **thank you** in Spanish?

gracias

adiós

How many crackers? Circle the correct number.

6 7 **8** 9 10

Fill in the shapes that have the letter **L**. What is it?

leaf

64
Answers on page 273.

Page 65

Find and circle the word **his**.

b e z h
c (h i s)
u z l y
w k p u

Which one is tired?

Is it fall or spring in this picture?

fall (spring)

Which one is the dog?

Fill in the missing number.

4 5 6 7 8 9

Answers on page 273.
65

Page 66

Find and circle the word **egg**.

f n l (e
i u o g
n v d g)
m w n z

How many cupcakes? Circle the correct number.

6 7 8 9 10

Circle the uppercase letters.

c (P) o
(D) (Q) a

Underline the words that begin with the letter **B**.

This is the **best book** about **bumblebees**.

Which one is purple?

66
Answers on page 273.

Page 67

Circle the one that begins with the letter **A**.

apple

Circle the woman.

Which letter comes next? Use the picture to help.

w x y

Fill in the shapes that have the letter **H**. What is it?

house

Answers on page 273.
67

273

Answers

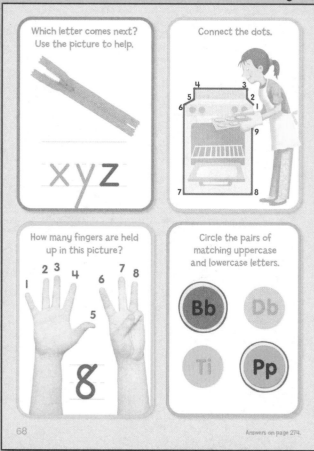

Which letter comes next? Use the picture to help.

x y **z**

Connect the dots.

How many fingers are held up in this picture?

2 3 4 6 7 8
1 5

8

Circle the pairs of matching uppercase and lowercase letters.

Bb Db

Ti **Pp**

Answers on page 274.

Find and circle the word **cup**.

a f i t
m **c** s k
r **u** l d
z **p** w s

Circle the person with blue eyes.

Is it fall or spring in this picture?

fall spring

Which one means **good night** in Spanish?

buenas noches

estrella

How many grasshoppers? Circle the correct number.

1 2 3 4 5 6 7 8 9 **10**

Answers on page 274.

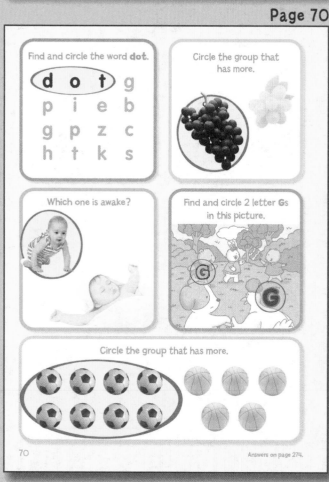

Find and circle the word **dot**.

d o t g
p i e b
g p z c
h t k s

Circle the group that has more.

Which one is awake?

Find and circle 2 letter **G**s in this picture.

Circle the group that has more.

Answers on page 274.

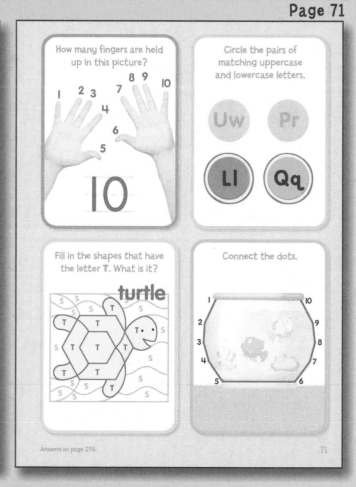

How many fingers are held up in this picture?

8 9
2 3 7 10
1 4
6
5

10

Circle the pairs of matching uppercase and lowercase letters.

Uw Pr

Ll **Qq**

Fill in the shapes that have the letter **T**. What is it?

turtle

Connect the dots.

Answers on page 274.

274

Page 72

What is this? Write its first letter.

Acorn

A

Follow the alphabet to connect the dots.

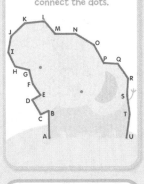

Fill in the shapes that have the letter **K**. What is it?

kite

Connect the two things that go together.

Answers on page 275.

Page 73

Circle the letter that is a vowel.

J G
S
I R

Are there more zebras or buses? Circle the answer.

zebras

buses

What meal do you eat after lunch?

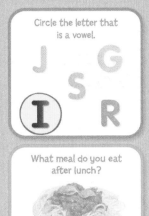

breakfast **(dinner)**

Find and circle the word **her**.

h	e	k	a	u
		v	s	p
e		t	y	g
r		d	e	o	f

Draw a triangle.

Page 74

Fill in the shapes to finish the pattern.

How many umbrellas can you find in this picture?

4

Answers on page 275.

Page 75

Color the spaces that have the number **5**.

Match the shoe to the right body part.

Circle the one who wears a crown.

queen

Are these shapes all triangles?

(yes) no

Trace the word.

orange

Answers

Answers on page 276.

Answers on page 276.

Answers on page 276.

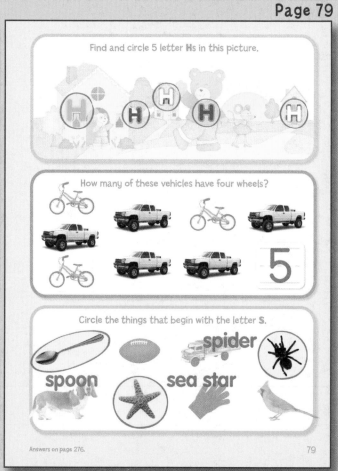

Answers on page 276.

Page 80

Find and circle 4 letter **I**s in this picture.

Connect the dots.

Put an **X** on the one that is different.

Answers on page 277.

Page 81

Is the hat on or off the dog's head?

on off

Circle the fisherman who caught the most fish.

Circle the group that has more.

Circle the letter that is a vowel.

D   Q
R
A   C

Circle the one that is hotter.

sun

Answers on page 277.

Page 82

How many acorns are there?

1

What do you brush before you go to bed?

feet
teeth

Match the shirt to the right body part.

Circle the one that is empty.

Trace the word.

white

Answers on page 277.

Page 83

How many apples are red?

3

Put an **X** on the one that is different.

Which helper puts out fires?

firefighter

What sound does the letter **F** make? Does this picture begin with the letter **F**?

yes
no

Feather begins with F.

Answers on page 277.

Answers

Circle the bunny in the hat.

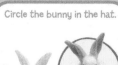

Underline the words that begin with the letter **R**.

The **race** was **really** fun for each **runner**.

Circle the letter that is a vowel.

Z U
X
J P

Sing the song, then answer the question.

On Top of Spaghetti

♪ On top of spaghetti, ♫
All covered with cheese,
I lost my poor meatball,
When somebody sneezed.

What was the spaghetti covered with?

pears (cheese) gum

Draw a square.

Circle the one that is made from wool.

scarf

Circle the plate that has more cupcakes.

How many brown things do you see?

7

What is this? Write its first letter.

Frog
F

How many monkeys are jumping on the bed?

4

Connect the two things that go together.

pencil

paper

Put an **X** on the one that is different.

Which animal belongs in this habitat?

penguin

Which one means **hello** in French?

(bonjour) merci

Color the spaces that have the number **2**.

Draw a line under the one that is heavier.

Fill in the shapes to finish the pattern.

Page 88

How many things in this picture start with the letter **T**?

5

turtle

tree

teacher

table

truck

88   Answers on page 279.

Page 89

Circle the squirrel that collected the most acorns.

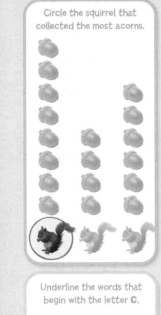

Circle the magazine.

Underline the words that begin with the letter **C**.

The <u>coat</u> in the <u>closet</u> has <u>candy</u> in its pockets.

Circle the one that is the opposite of left.

Answers on page 279.   89

Page 90

Is this temperature hot or cold?

92°F

(hot)

cold

How many shirts have dots?

2

Connect the two things that go together.

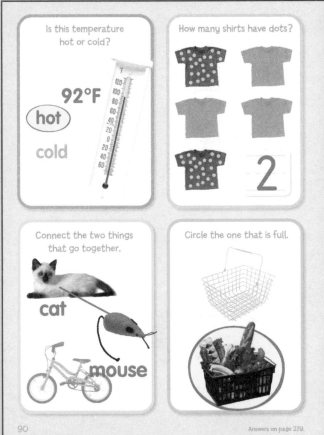

cat

mouse

Circle the one that is full.

90   Answers on page 279.

Page 91

Which would we wear in the summer?

sandals

Circle the things that begin with the letter **D**.

doughnut

dog

Underline the words that begin with the letter **M**.

<u>My mother</u> <u>makes muffins</u> on <u>Mondays</u>.

Circle the plant that is the youngest.

Circle the letter that is a vowel.

I N Q C H

Answers

Circle the things that begin with the letter **B**.

bell
butterfly
bow
bear

Find and circle 4 letter **P**s in this picture.

Answers on page 280.

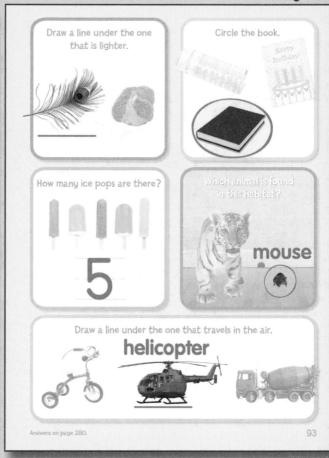

Draw a line under the one that is lighter.

Circle the book.

Happy Birthday!

How many ice pops are there?

5

Which animal is found in this habitat?

mouse

Draw a line under the one that travels in the air.

helicopter

Answers on page 280.

Circle the letter that is a vowel.

M P
O
W K

Underline the words that begin with the letter **H**.

He was **hunting** for **honey** on the **hillside**.

Circle the one you use to cut food.

knife

Circle the things that begin with the letter **C**.

carrot

castle

Circle the xylophone.

Answers on page 280.

Which person is the tallest?

Connect the two things that go together.

leash

dog

Which animal belongs in this habitat?

cow

Answers on page 280.

Answers

Page 96

What sound does the letter **B** make? Does this picture begin with the letter **B**?

yes no

Ball begins with B.

Circle the one that begins with the letter **O**.

octopus

Which person do you see when you're sick?

doctor

What is this? Write its first letter.

Guitar

G

Answers on page 281.

Page 97

How many blue things do you see?

5

Where does the President of the United States live?

the White House

Find and circle 4 letter **W**s in the picture.

W **W** **W** **W**

Answers on page 281.

Page 98

Which animal belongs in this habitat?

polar bear

How many birds are there?

2

Draw a line to cut the apple in half.

Put an **X** on the vase that has fewer flowers.

Trace the word.

blue

Answers on page 281.

Page 99

Circle the one that finishes the pattern.

Trace the word, then color the picture.

cat

Circle the person who is taller.

What sound does the letter **K** make? Does this picture begin with the letter **K**?

yes no

Kite begins with K.

Answers on page 281.

Answers

Draw a line under the rock that is smooth.

Sing the song, then answer the question.

Buckle My Shoe

One, two, buckle my shoe;
Three, four, shut the door;
♪ Five, six, pick up sticks; ♪
Seven, eight, lay them straight;
Nine, ten, do it again! ♫

What do you pick up after five and six?

shoes hats (sticks)

Circle the letter that is a vowel.

P (E) B C R

Draw a line under the puppy in the middle.

Circle the seatbelt.

Answers on page 282.

Circle the leaf.

Circle the ballet shoes.

How many chairs are there?

3

Draw a line under the one that is heavier.

Fill in the shapes to finish the pattern.

Answers on page 282.

Color the spaces that have the number **1**.

Which animal belongs in this habitat?

fish

Circle the one that is empty.

Put an **X** on the one that is different.

Which holiday are these children celebrating?

Halloween

Answers on page 282.

Are there more ducks or ducklings? Circle the answer.

ducks (ducklings)

What is this? Write its first letter.

Hammer
H

What sound does the letter **N** make? Does this picture begin with the letter **N**?

yes (no)
Rabbit begins with R.

Connect the two things that go together.

shovel

pail

Answers on page 282.

Page 104

Underline the words that begin with the letter **L**.

Let's lounge on the **lawn** after **lunch**.

Draw a line under the one that is lighter.

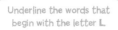

Which one means **stop**?

Draw a diamond.

Put an **X** on the basket that has fewer strawberries.

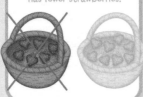

Circle the letter that is a vowel.

Ⓐ V
F
B N

Page 105

What is this? Write its first letter.

Bee

B

Circle the one that begins with the letter **C**.

crab

Circle the things that begin with the letter **L**.

ladder   **lion**

lamp

lettuce

Page 106

What sound does the letter **C** make? Does this picture begin with the letter **C**?

yes
(no)

Dog begins with D.

Circle the helmet.

What is this? Write its first letter.

Ice

I

Circle the group that has more.

Page 107

Circle the fishbowl that has more fish.

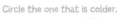

Connect the two things that go together.

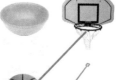

Circle the letters that are consonants.

I   Ⓥ
A
Ⓜ   Ⓣ

Circle the one that is colder.

Underline the words that begin with the letter **N**.

Nick never found the **note** that **Nancy** sent.

Answers

How many balloons are there?

6

What is the girl celebrating?

birthday

Circle the things that begin with the letter **H**.

hammer

heart

hot dog

What sound does the letter **L** make? Does this picture begin with the letter **L**?

yes no

Lizard begins with **L**.

Find and circle the word **go** in the picture.

Circle the one that finishes the pattern.

Circle the roots.

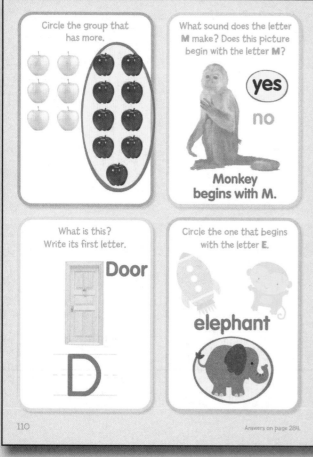

Circle the group that has more.

What sound does the letter **M** make? Does this picture begin with the letter **M**?

yes

no

Monkey begins with M.

What is this? Write its first letter.

Door

D

Circle the one that begins with the letter **E**.

elephant

Which person is older?

Which animal belongs in this habitat?

ant

Which one means **thank you** in French?

au revoir **merci**

Color the spaces that have the number **4**.

Fill in the shapes to finish the pattern.

Page 112

Trace the word.

green

Draw a line under the one that travels on the road.
car

Connect the ones that are the same.

What sound does the letter **J** make? Does this picture begin with the letter **J**?

yes **(no)**
Watermelon begins with W.

112   Answers on page 285.

Page 113

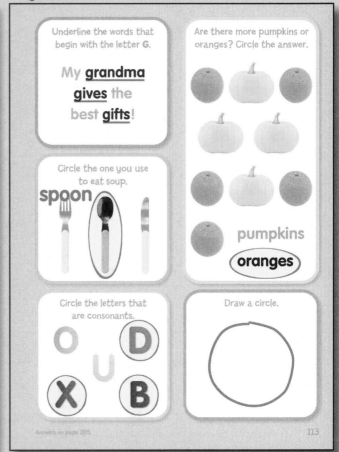

Underline the words that begin with the letter **G**.

My **grandma** **gives** the best **gifts**!

Are there more pumpkins or oranges? Circle the answer.

pumpkins
(oranges)

Circle the one you use to eat soup.
spoon

Circle the letters that are consonants.

O **D**
U
X **B**

Draw a circle.

Answers on page 285.   113

Page 114

Which one flies to the moon?
space shuttle

Who takes care of barnyard animals?
farmer

Which one means **excuse me** in French?
pardon   de rien

Circle the group that has more.

How many chicks are there?
4

114   Answers on page 285.

Page 115

How many diamonds are there?
3

Which animal belongs in this habitat?
dog

Find and circle the letter **D** in this picture.

Trace the word, then color the picture.
top

Answers on page 285.   115

Answers

Underline the words that begin with the letter **V**.

<u>Vivian's</u> <u>voice</u> was <u>very</u> pretty with the <u>violin</u>.

Put an **X** on the group that has fewer pencils.

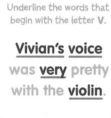

Draw a line to cut the orange in half.

Draw a line under the rock that is rough.

Circle the letter that is a vowel.

K   F
   D
G   **O**

116

Answers on page 286.

Put an **X** on the animal that is not an insect.

Circle the one that finishes the pattern.

Color the spaces that have the number **3**.

What meal do you eat before lunch?

dinner (**breakfast**)

Fill in the shapes to finish the pattern.

Answers on page 286.

117

What color bead comes next? Circle the answer.

How many rectangles do you see in the house?

6

Connect the two things that go together.

racket   ball

Circle the one that begins with the letter **P**.

pear

118

Answers on page 286.

Find and circle 7 letter **Z**s in this picture.

How many of these foods are fruits?

apple   plum

orange   banana   4

Answers on page 286.

119

Answers

Page 120

Circle the letter that is a vowel.

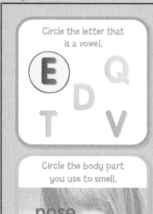

Circle the body part you use to smell.

nose

Underline the words that begin with the letter **D**.

The **December** school **dance** will be **during** the **day**.

Trace the word, then color the picture.

pig

Draw a line under the easel.

Answers on page 287.

120

Page 121

Circle the one that is floating.

Circle the one that begins with the letter **I**.

ice cream

Circle the plate that has more cookies.

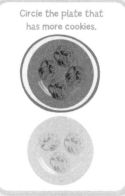

Write the first letter of this word.

Dog

Answers on page 287.

121

Page 122

Circle the one that matches the fruits in the square.

Circle the Earth.

Who lives in the tepee?

Circle the one that is the opposite of short.

tall

122

Answers on page 287.

Page 123

Circle the one that finishes the pattern.

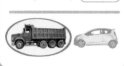

Which person is the shortest?

Which one would we wear in the snow?

coat

What sound does the letter **T** make? Does this picture begin with the letter **T**?

yes   no

Tiger begins with T.

Answers on page 287.

123

Answers

Page 124

What sound does the letter **X** make? Does this picture begin with the letter **X**?

yes **no**

Flower begins with F.

What is this? Write its first letter.

Lemon

L

Connect the two things that go together.

fishbowl

fish

Where do we buy food?

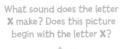

grocery store

MARKET

Answers on page 288.

Page 125

Which animal belongs in this habitat?

Which animal belongs in this habitat?

swan

Find and circle the word **bus** in this picture.

SCHOOL BUS

Put an **X** on the one that is different.

What is the cat wearing?

hat

shoe

How many strawberries are there?

8

Answers on page 288.

Page 126

Circle the letters that are consonants.

G **R** A O E

Draw a star.

Underline the word that begins with the letter **X**.

Suzie needs an X-ray of her arm.

Sing the song, then answer the question.

Where Is Thumbkin?

♪ Where is Thumbkin?
Where is Thumbkin? ♪
♪ Here I am!
Here I am!
How are you this morning?
Very well, I thank you.
Run away. ♪
Run away.

Which finger is Thumbkin?

thumb pinky

Circle the stem of the plant.

Answers on page 288.

Page 127

Circle the one that begins with the letter **S**.

snake

What color button comes next? Circle the answer.

Are there more gorillas or goats? Circle the answer.

gorillas goats

Write the first letter of this word.

Gift

Answers on page 288.

Page 128

Trace the word, then color the picture.

bee

Which one means **good night** in French?

bonne nuit bonjour

Circle the one that matches the animal in the square.

What sound does the letter **P** make? Does this picture begin with the letter **P**?

yes no

Pig begins with P.

Answers on page 289.

Page 129

Find and circle the word **up** in this picture.

THIS END UP

Are these shapes all squares?

yes **no**

Find and circle the letter **T** in this picture.

T

Color the spaces that have the number **7**.

Fill in the shapes to finish the pattern.

★ ☆ ★ ☆ | ★ ☆ ★ ☆ ★ |

Answers on page 289.

Page 130

Circle the tap shoes.

What is the duck riding?

truck bike

How many sides does a triangle have? Write the number.

3

Circle the one that is hotter.

Which holiday is this girl celebrating?

Valentine's Day

Answers on page 289.

Page 131

Trace the word, then color the picture.

sun

Connect the ones that are the same.

Circle the group that has more.

What is this? Write its first letter.

Pizza

P

Answers on page 289.

Answers

Circle the group that has more.

What sound does the letter **R** make? Does this picture begin with the letter **R**?

yes

no

Toothbrush begins with T.

Circle the one that begins with the letter **W**.

whale

Circle the piano.

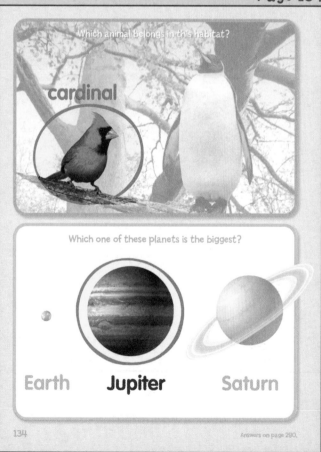

132

Answers on page 290.

Circle the letter that is a vowel.

J   G
   S
I   R

Circle the instrument students played most.

Underline the words that begin with the letter **F**.

The **family** watches **fireworks** while they **fish**.

Circle the body part you use to touch.

hand

Draw a line to cut the square in half.

Answers on page 290.

133

Which animal belongs in this habitat?

cardinal

Which one of these planets is the biggest?

Earth   **Jupiter**   Saturn

134

Answers on page 290.

Trace the word, then color the picture.

owl

Connect the ones that are the same.

Which person prepares food?

chef

What is this? Write its first letter.

Umbrella

U

Answers on page 290.

135

290

Page 136

Are these shapes all hearts?
yes (no)

Find and circle the word **ice** in this picture.

Circle the tree that has more apples.

Color the spaces that have the number **6**.

Trace the word.
black

Page 137

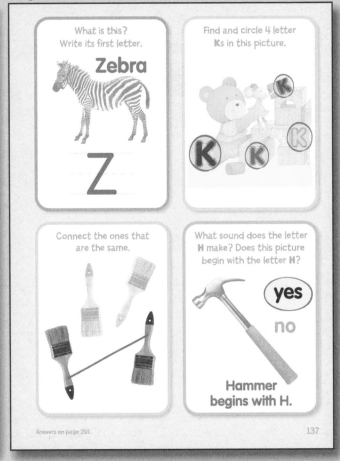

What is this? Write its first letter.
Zebra
Z

Find and circle 4 letter **K**s in this picture.

Connect the ones that are the same.

What sound does the letter **H** make? Does this picture begin with the letter **H**?
yes
no
Hammer begins with H.

Page 138

Circle the one that matches the fruit in the square.

What sound does the letter **y** make? Does this picture begin with the letter **y**?
yes   no
Yarn begins with Y.

Write the first letter of this word.
Pig

Chart each item below.

Page 139

Which child is not following the rules?
He did not stop.

How many goldfish are there?
9

Circle the one that's exactly the same as the one in the circle.

Answers

Page 140

Draw a line under the one that travels on tracks.

train

Fill in the shapes to finish the pattern.

Which person keeps you and your neighborhood safe?

police officer

What is this?
Write its first letter.

Onion

○

Answers on page 292.

Page 141

Circle the letters that are consonants.

A P O
K F

Sing the song, then answer the question.

Yankee Doodle

Yankee Doodle went to town,
Riding on a pony.
He stuck a feather in his cap,
And called it macaroni.

What did Yankee Doodle stick a feather in?

pony   town   (cap)

Circle the one that is full.

Underline the words that begin with the letter **J**.

In **January**, **Joyce** wears a **jeweled jacket**.

Draw a line under the one that is heavier.

Answers on page 292.

141

Page 142

Find and circle 3 letter **B**s in this picture.

Circle the one that finishes the pattern.

Which one would a baker wear?

Answers on page 292.

Page 143

Connect the two things that go together.

SANTA CLAUS
123 CANDY CANE LANE
NORTH POLE

What sound does the letter **V** make? Does this picture begin with the letter **V**?

yes

no

Vase begins with V.

Which person is younger?

What is this?
Write its first letter.

Cat

C

Answers on page 292.

143

292

Page 144

Circle the knee pads.

Uh-oh! Hippo knocked the plant over. What should he say?

Thank you.

(I'm sorry.)

Circle the letters that are consonants.

(T) P (I) E (P) (K)

Underline the words that begin with the letter **T**.

The **track** **team** practiced for **two** hours.

Answers on page 293.

Page 145

Are there more orange or pink dinosaurs? Circle the answer.

(orange) pink

Is this temperature hot or cold?

hot

(cold)

10°F

Write the first letter of this word.

Kite

Which person helps you find books?

librarian

Answers on page 293.

Page 146

What sound does the letter **G** make? Does this picture begin with the letter **G**?

(yes)

no

Goat begins with G.

Put an **X** on the one that is different.

Are there more purple or green crayons? Circle the answer.

(purple) green

What is this? Write its first letter.

Saw

S

Answers on page 293.

Page 147

Which one means **yes** in French?

(oui) merci

Find and circle the letter **Z** in the soup.

Are these shapes all diamonds?

(yes) no

What's sitting on the dog?

dog (frog)

Fill in the shapes to finish the pattern.

Answers on page 293.

Answers

Find and circle the word **stop** in this picture.

Trace the word, then color the picture.

COW

Write the first letter of this word.

Bat

Circle the one that matches the robot in the square.

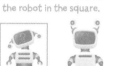

148

Answers on page 294.

How many sides does a diamond have? Write the number.

4

Which person helps you cross the street?

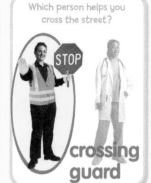

crossing guard

Which animal belongs in this habitat?

chimpanzee

Answers on page 294.

149

Circle the one that finishes the pattern.

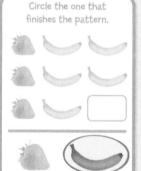

What is this? Write its first letter.

Jump rope

J

What sound does the letter **W** make? Does this picture begin with the letter **W**?

yes   no

Wagon begins with W.

Put an **X** on the one that is different.

150

Answers on page 294.

Circle the ones that begin with the letter **V**.

violin

vase

van

Circle the group that has more.

Circle the bag that is full.

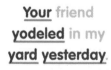

Underline the words that begin with the letter **Y**.

Your friend **yodeled** in my **yard yesterday**.

Answers on page 294.

151

294

Answers

Page 152

Find and circle 7 letter **C**s in this picture.

Can you name each of the 7 objects?

curtain · clock · cat · cookie · cup · cake · carrot

Which person helps at a restaurant?

server

Which one goes with the toothbrush?

toothpaste

152

Answers on page 295.

Page 153

What is the boy wearing on his head?

ring

crown

Write the first letter of this word.

Tree

How many squares are there?

7

Put an **X** on the one that is different.

Answers on page 295.

153

Page 154

Draw a line under the person who is first in line.

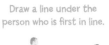

Circle the plant that is older.

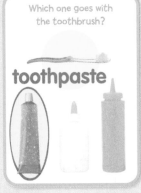

Underline the words that begin with the letter **K**.

The **kettle** in the **kitchen** is **kept** on the stove.

Circle the letters that are consonants.

E · **B** · o · **Q** · **D**

Circle the one you see at night.

moon

154

Answers on page 295.

Page 155

Put an **X** on the one that is different.

Circle the one that begins with the letter **K**.

kite

Circle the one that matches the car in the square.

What is this? Write its first letter.

Yogurt

Y

Answers on page 295.

155

295

Answers

What sound does the letter **Q** make? Does this picture begin with the letter **Q**?

yes

no

Queen begins with Q.

Circle the one that is the opposite of big.

little

Circle the drums.

Write the first letter of this word.

Fish

156

Answers on page 296.

Trace the word.

red

Sing the song, then answer the question.

Old MacDonald

Old MacDonald had a farm,
E, I, E, I, O.
And on this farm he had a
pig, E, I, E, I, O.
With an oink-oink here and
an oink-oink there,
Here an oink, there an oink,
everywhere an oink-oink.
Old MacDonald had a farm,
E, I, E, I, O.

What did Old MacDonald have?

a farm   a factory   a school

Answers on page 296.   157

Match the coat to the right body part.

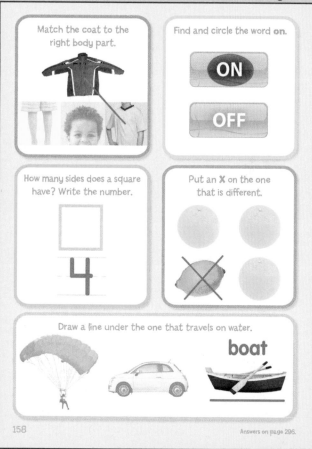

Find and circle the word **on**.

ON

OFF

How many sides does a square have? Write the number.

4

Put an **X** on the one that is different.

Draw a line under the one that travels on water.

boat

158

Answers on page 296.

What is this? Write its first letter.

Rake

R

Put an **X** on the one that is different.

Connect the ones that are the same.

Trace the word, then color the picture.

bus

Answers on page 296.   159

Page 160

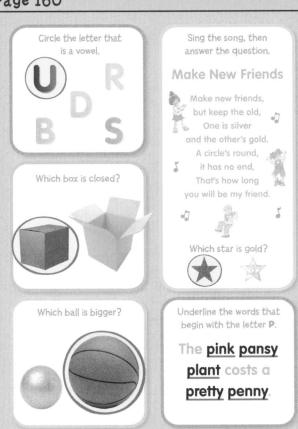

Circle the letter that is a vowel.

U R D B S

Which box is closed?

Which ball is bigger?

Sing the song, then answer the question.

Make New Friends

Make new friends, but keep the old, One is silver and the other's gold. A circle's round, it has no end, That's how long you will be my friend.

Which star is gold?

Underline the words that begin with the letter **P**.

The **pink pansy plant** costs a **pretty penny**.

Answers on page 297.

Page 161

Color the spaces that have the number **9**.

Put an **X** on the stand that has fewer cupcakes.

Draw a line under the one that is heavier.

Circle the one that is the opposite of up.

down

Fill in the shapes to finish the pattern.

▲ ▲ △ △ △   ▲ ▲ △ △ △

Answers on page 297.

Page 162

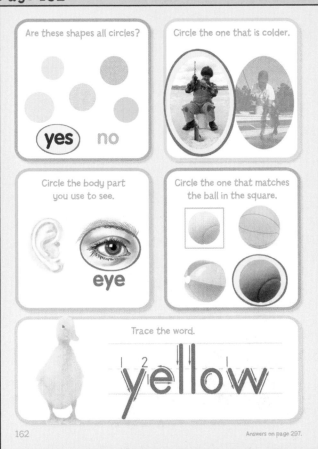

Are these shapes all circles?

yes no

Circle the one that is colder.

Circle the body part you use to see.

eye

Circle the one that matches the ball in the square.

Trace the word.

yellow

Answers on page 297.

Page 163

Connect the two things that go together.

ring

hand

What is this? Write its first letter.

Watermelon

W

Find and circle 5 letter **S**s in this picture.

S S S S S

Which person cleans your teeth?

STOP

dentist

Answers on page 297.

Answers

Draw a line to cut the cake in half.

Which one will stick to the magnet?

key

Underline the words that begin with the letter **W**.

Willy **was** a **wonderful** **worker** every **Wednesday**.

Circle the car that faces front.

Circle the letters that are consonants.

P U I X L

Answers on page 298.

Which person is in the army?

soldier

What is this? Write its first letter.

Violin

V

Circle the ice cream that was ordered the most.

Answers on page 298.

Write the first letter of this word.

Star

Circle the one that finishes the pattern.

Which one means **good-bye** in French?

au revoir   oui

What is this? Write its first letter.

Elephant

E

166

Answers on page 298.

Sing the song, then answer the question.

The Ants Go Marching

The ants go marching one by one, hurrah, hurrah!
The ants go marching one by one, hurrah, hurrah!
The ants go marching one by one,
The little one stops to suck his thumb,
And they all go marching down to the ground
To get out of the rain, BOOM! BOOM! BOOM!

What were the ants trying to get out of?

work   (the rain)   trouble

Which team won the game?

HOME   GUESTS

Answers on page 298.

Page 168

How many leaves are there?

7

Which animal belongs in this habitat?

horse

Answers on page 299.

Page 169

Find and circle 5 letter **X**s in this picture.

What is this?
Write its first letter.

Kangaroo

K

What sound does the letter **Z** make? Does this picture begin with the letter **Z**?

yes **no**

Kiwi begins with K.

Where do we go if we are sick?

hospital

169

Page 170

Circle the one that begins with the letter **L**.

lion

Put an **X** on the one that is different.

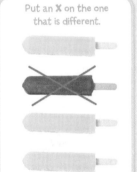

Trace the word, then color the picture.

fox

Find and circle the word **no**.

NO
PARKING
ANY
TIME

Answers on page 299.

Page 171

Color the spaces that have the number **8**.

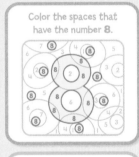

Circle the one that is hotter.

Put an **X** on the tree that has fewer leaves.

What is the bear holding?

pear apple

Which holiday is this boy celebrating?

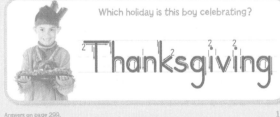
Thanksgiving

171

Answers

Circle the newspaper.

Which one would we wear in the rain?

raincoat

Circle the one that finishes the pattern.

What is this?
Write its first letter.

Turtle

T

Answers on page 300.

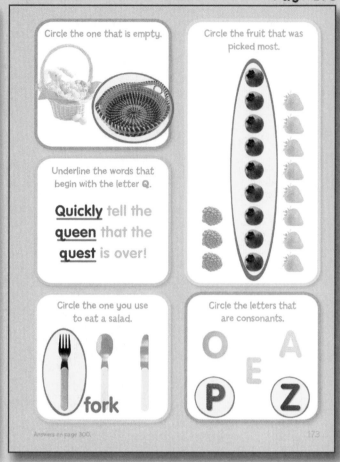

Circle the one that is empty.

Circle the fruit that was picked most.

Underline the words that begin with the letter **Q**.

Quickly tell the **queen** that the **quest** is over!

Circle the one you use to eat a salad.

fork

Circle the letters that are consonants.

O E A

P Z

Answers on page 300.

Match the hat to the right body part.

Circle the one that is colder.

snow

Put an **X** on the one that is different.

Are these shapes all stars?

yes **no**

Which of these is a musical instrument?

drum

Answers on page 300.

Connect the two things that go together.

water

plant

How many yellow stars are in the sky?

10

What is this?
Write its first letter.

X-ray

X

What sound does the letter **S** make? Does this picture begin with the letter **S**?

yes no

Sun begins with S.

Answers on page 300.

Page 176

Find and circle 6 letter **F**s in this picture.

Circle the one that begins with the letter **T**.

train

What is this? Write its first letter.

Monkey

M

Which person helps sick animals?

veterinarian

Page 177

Circle the one that's exactly the same as the top crayon.

Put an **X** on the one that will not stick to the magnet.

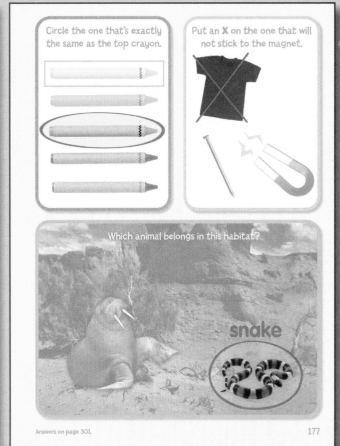

Which animal belongs in this habitat?

snake

Page 178

Circle the letters that are consonants.

U I E
M N

What animal is in the boat?

cat goat

Draw a line under the person who is last in line.

Color the spaces that have the number **10**.

Which holiday is this girl celebrating?

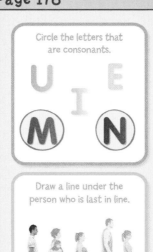

4th of July

Page 179

Which team lost the game?

HOME 5
GUESTS 7

Fill in the shapes to finish the pattern.

○○○○ ■■ ○○○○○ ■ ■ ○○○○ ■ ■

What is this? Write its first letter.

Question mark

Q

Write the first letter of this word.

Car

Answers

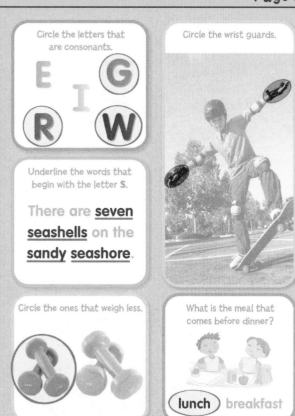

Circle the letters that are consonants.

E I G R W

Underline the words that begin with the letter **S**.

There are **seven seashells** on the **sandy seashore**.

Circle the ones that weigh less.

What is the meal that comes before dinner?

lunch breakfast

Answers on page 302.

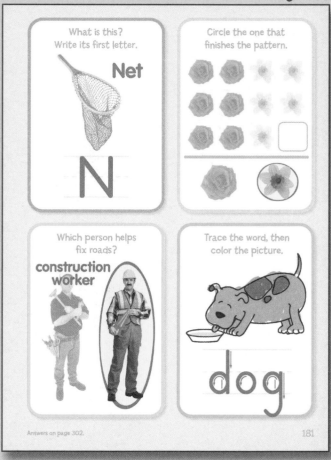

What is this? Write its first letter.

Net

N

Circle the one that finishes the pattern.

Which person helps fix roads?

construction worker

Trace the word, then color the picture.

dog

Answers on page 302.

Find and circle 2 letter **X**s in the picture.

Connect the two things that go together.

bike

helmet

Chart each item below.

	1	2	3	4	5
	✓	✓			
	✓	✓	✓	✓	

Circle the letter.

Answers on page 302.

Read the nursery rhyme, then answer the questions.

Little Miss Muffet

Little Miss Muffet
Sat on a tuffet,
Eating her curds and whey.
There came a big spider,
Who sat down beside her,
And frightened
Miss Muffet away.

What sat down beside Little Miss Muffet?

spider

What was Little Miss Muffet sitting on?

tuffet

Answers on page 302.

Answers

Page 184

Trace the missing letter. What is the word?

sat

Circle the dog that is inside the doghouse.

inside

Circle the tomato.

Underline the words that begin with the letter **Z**.

<u>**Zack**</u> saw <u>**zero**</u> hippos at the <u>**zoo**</u>.

Trace the missing letter. What is the word?

tap

Answers on page 303.

Page 185

Match the sock to the right body part.

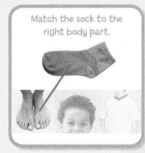

Circle the American flag.

What is the opposite of dark?

light

Circle the guitar.

Circle the things that begin with the letter **W**.

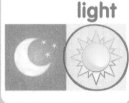

witch   **waffle**

wolf

Answers on page 303.

Page 186

Which one of these planets is the smallest?

Venus   Saturn   Neptune

Circle the things that begin with the letter **G**.

grapes   **goose**

glasses

How many hot dogs are there?

10

Answers on page 303.

Page 187

Which word means **you're welcome** in French?

de rien   au revoir

Draw a line under the things you need to paint a picture.

Connect the two things that go together.

baseball

glove

Find and circle the word **pet** in this picture.

Pet Shop

Answers on page 303.

Answers

Page 192

Match the jeans to the right body part.

Connect the pictures that rhyme.

vest

nest

Find and circle 3 letter **R**s in the picture.

Connect the things that go together.

Answers on page 305.

Page 193

Trace the missing letter. What is the word?

pet

Circle the things that begin with the letter **F**.

flag   feather

fork

Solve the addition problem.

$1 + 2 = 3$

Which signal means walk?

Trace the missing letter. What is the word?

10 ten

Answers on page 305.

Page 194

Draw a line under the one that travels on snow.

sled

Solve the addition problem.

$+ = 3$

Which one is the opposite of fast?

slow

Connect the pictures that rhyme.

moon

spoon

Answers on page 305.

Page 195

Read the story, then answer the question.

Three Little Pigs

Once there were three little pigs. The first built a house of straw, and the second built a house of sticks; the third pig built a house of bricks. One day a wolf came to all three houses. He blew down the house of straw and the house of sticks! But when he tried to blow the brick house down, he couldn't. The third pig had outsmarted the wolf!

What did the second pig build his house with?

sticks

Answers on page 305.

Answers

Which animal is feeling sick?

Trace the picture. What shape is it?

circle
oval

Solve the subtraction problem.

3 - 1 = 2

Circle the corn.

Draw a line under the sign that means a fire station is nearby.

H

Answers on page 306.

Which dog is the opposite of wet?

dry

Which toy costs more?

$3
$4

Circle the monkey in the middle.

Connect the pictures that rhyme.

mouse
house

Answers on page 306.

Read the nursery rhyme, then answer the questions.

The Cat and the Fiddle

Hey, diddle, diddle,
The cat and the fiddle,
The cow jumped
Over the moon.
The little dog laughed
To see such sport,
And the dish ran away
With the spoon.

What did the cow jump over?
moon

What instrument does the cat play?

fiddle

Answers on page 306.

Circle the things that begin with the letter U.

unicycle
umbrella
unicorn

Solve the addition problem.
 + = 2

Match the word to the correct picture.
jar

Which children are skipping?

Answers on page 306.

Page 200

Trace the missing letter. What is the word?

see

Circle the ballerina.

Solve the addition problem.

1 + 1 = 2

Circle the paint can that is open.

Trace the missing letter. What is the word?

fin

  Answers on page 307.

Page 201

Number the events in the correct order.

2   3   1

Which sign tells you how to get out of a building?

EXIT

Solve the subtraction problem.

4 - 2 = 2

Page 202

Trace the picture. What shape is it?

triangle
(square)

Circle the green beans.

How many pennies?

7

Fill in half of the circle.

Match the word to the correct picture.

walrus

Page 203

Which one is the opposite of in?

out

Which word means **head** in Spanish?

sol

(cabeza)

Connect the pictures that rhyme.

pie

tie

Connect the two things that go together.

table

chair

Answers

Connect the pictures that rhyme.

duck

truck

Which toy costs less?

$5

$2

Circle two things that help plants grow.

sun

rain

Circle the one that starts the same way as **egg**.

eraser

Answers on page 308.

Read the story, then answer the question.

Rapunzel

Once there was an evil witch who had a very tall tower. She kept Rapunzel locked up in the tower. Rapunzel had very long hair. One day, a handsome prince found Rapunzel and climbed up her hair to the tower. Then he helped her escape and they lived happily ever after.

Where did Rapunzel live?

tower

Answers on page 308.

Solve the addition problem.

+ = **4**

Which one can you recycle?

can

Which one is the opposite of light?

dark

Circle the one that starts the same way as **igloo**.

ice cream

Answers on page 308.

Connect the pictures that rhyme.

can

fan

Circle the bee that is under the flower.

What do you say when you politely ask for something?

please no

What time is it?

3:00 5:00

Answers on page 308.

Page 208

Which fruit has two pieces that are the same?

Draw a line under the sign that means be careful.

Trace the missing letter. What is the word?

hot

Solve the addition problem.

$1 + 3 = 4$

Page 209

Read the nursery rhyme, then answer the questions.

Little Bo Peep

Little Bo Peep
has lost her sheep,
And can't tell where
to find them.
Leave them alone,
And they'll come home,
Wagging their tails
behind them.

What did Little Bo Peep lose?

sheep

Circle the sheep's tail.

Page 210

Connect the pictures that rhyme.

cat
bat

Which one is the opposite of over?

under

What time is it?

3:00   (8:00)

Circle the person who is shorter.

Page 211

Circle the computer screen.

Solve the addition problem.

$1 + 4 = 5$

Circle the flag of Mexico.

Trace the picture. What shape is it?

triangle
square

Which one is a fruit?
peach

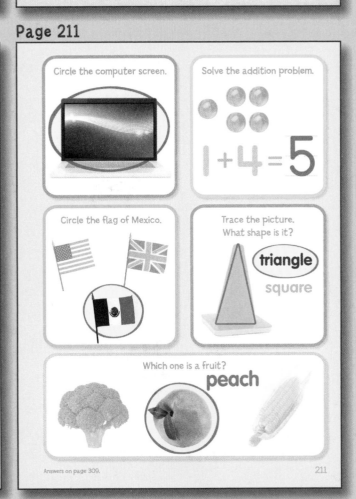

Answers

Page 212

Trace the missing letter. What is the word?

b i t

Which one tells you a train is nearby?

Solve the addition problem.

2 + 3 = 5

Fill in one fourth of the square.

Trace the missing letter. What is the word?

s e w

212

Answers on page 310.

Page 213

Solve the subtraction problem.

5 - 2 = 3

Match the word to the correct picture.

horse

Which word means **hands** in Spanish?

manos

ojos

Connect the pictures that rhyme.

bell

shell

Answers on page 310.

213

Page 214

What do you say when someone gives you a present?

thank you   sorry

Which one is the opposite of laugh?

cry

Circle the one on the bottom.

Connect the pictures that rhyme.

king

ring

214

Answers on page 310.

Page 215

When plants start to grow, what season is it?

fall   spring

Match the word to the correct picture.

hat

Number the events in the correct order.

2   1   3

Answers on page 310.

215

310

Page 216

Circle the toys that cost the same.

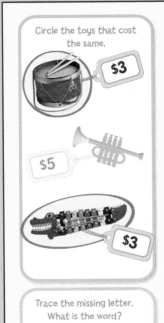

$3

$5

$3

Draw a line under the sign that means boys' washroom.

Trace the missing letter. What is the word?

red

Trace the missing letter. What is the word?

sip

216

Answers on page 311.

Page 217

Which one has three pieces that are the same?

Connect the pictures that rhyme.

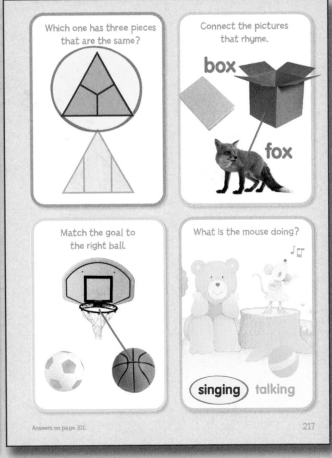

box

fox

Match the goal to the right ball.

What is the mouse doing?

(singing) talking

Answers on page 311.

217

Page 218

Read the story, then answer the question.

The Ugly Duckling

Once upon a time, a mother duck had some baby ducklings. All of the ducklings were little and yellow, except for one. He was big and gray. Everyone teased him and called him ugly.

When the ugly duckling grew up, he found out that he wasn't a duck at all! He was a swan. That was why he looked different from the other ducklings. He met other swans like him and they lived happily ever after.

What color was the ugly duckling?

(gray) green yellow

218

Answers on page 311.

Page 219

Trace the missing letter. What is the word?

dig

Circle the mouse.

Solve the subtraction problem.

3 - 2 = 1

Circle the cauliflower.

Trace the missing letter. What is the word?

leg

Answers on page 311.

219

Answers

Which president is on the one dollar bill?

George Washington

Connect the pictures that rhyme.

dog

frog

What time is it?

(7:00)   9:00

Which one is the opposite of sour?

sweet

Answers on page 312.

Circle the longer snake.

Trace the picture. What shape is it?

oval

star

How many dimes?

6

Match the word to the correct picture.

dinosaur

Draw a line under the sign that means a playground is nearby.

Answers on page 312.

Number the events in the correct order.

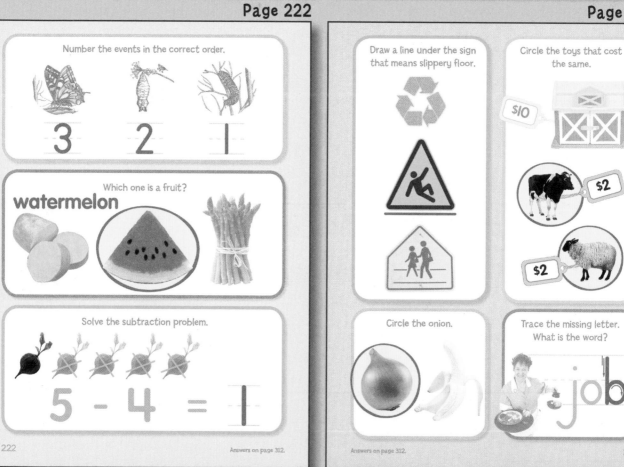

3   2   1

Which one is a fruit?

watermelon

Solve the subtraction problem.

5 − 4 = 1

Answers on page 312.

Draw a line under the sign that means slippery floor.

Circle the toys that cost the same.

$10

$2

$2

Circle the onion.

Trace the missing letter. What is the word?

job

Answers on page 312.

Page 224

Trace the missing letter. What is the word?

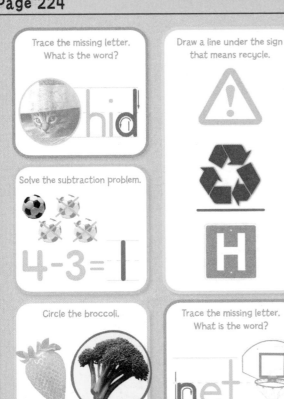

hid

Draw a line under the sign that means recycle.

Solve the subtraction problem.

4 - 3 = 1

Circle the broccoli.

Trace the missing letter. What is the word?

net

Page 225

Connect the pictures that rhyme.

snake

cake

Circle the one that starts the same way as **bat**.

butterfly

Circle the gifts on the left.

Which word means **water** in Spanish?

agua

leche

Page 226

Number the events in the correct order.

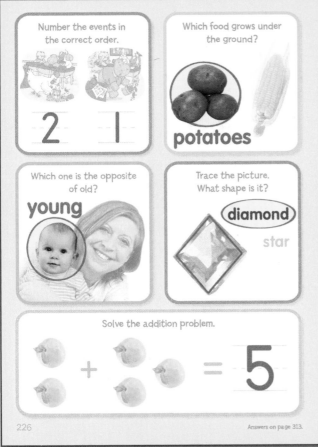

2   1

Which food grows under the ground?

potatoes

Which one is the opposite of old?

young

Trace the picture. What shape is it?

diamond

star

Solve the addition problem.

+ = 5

Page 227

Circle the plane that is above the cloud.

Connect the pictures that rhyme.

star

car

Circle the one that starts the same way as **door**.

duck

Circle the keyboard.

Answers

Match the goal to the right ball.

Which of these grows on a tree?

lemon

How many quarters?

3

Circle the bin you would use to recycle this bottle.

Read the nursery rhyme, then answer the question.

Little Boy Blue

Little Boy Blue,
Come blow your horn.
The sheep's in the meadow,
The cow's in the corn.

Where's the little boy
Who looks after the sheep?
Under the haystack
Fast asleep.

Where was Little Boy Blue sleeping?

under the haystack

228

Answers on page 314.

Answers on page 314.

229

Connect the pictures that rhyme.

bee
tree

Which toy costs less?

$9
$10

Which one should you use to wipe your nose?

tissue

Circle the one that starts the same way as **jack**.

jellyfish

Trace the missing letter. What is the word?

arm

Circle the chopsticks.

Solve the subtraction problem.

$$5 - 1 = 4$$

Trace the missing letter. What is the word?

bug

Circle the lettuce.

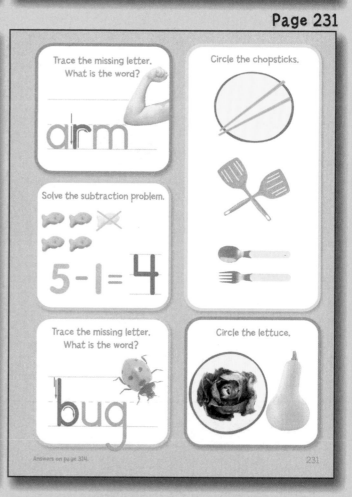

230

Answers on page 314.

Answers on page 314.

231

314

Answers

Page 232

Match the word to the correct picture.

boat

Which one can you recycle?

newspaper

Circle the flag of Canada.

What should you do when you cough?

Which one is a fruit?

strawberry

232

Answers on page 315.

Page 233

Match the ball to the right equipment.

Which toy costs more?

$8

$10

Circle the one that starts the same way as **uncle**.

umbrella

Which one is the opposite of glad?

mad

Answers on page 315.

233

Page 234

Read the nursery rhyme, then answer the questions.

Humpty Dumpty

Humpty Dumpty sat on a wall;
Humpty Dumpty had a great fall!
All the king's horses
And all the king's men
Couldn't put Humpty
together again.

What did Humpty Dumpty fall from?

wall

Did Humpty Dumpty get put back together again?

yes

no

234

Answers on page 315.

Page 235

Match the word to the correct picture.

star

Connect the pictures that rhyme.

clock

sock

Which one is the opposite of clean?

dirty

What instrument is the girl playing?

guitar violin

Answers on page 315.

235

315

Answers

Match the word to the correct picture.

truck

Circle the one that starts the same way as **nut**.

nest

Which one is the opposite of small?

big

Match the ball to the right equipment.

Answers on page 316.

What numbers would you dial in an emergency?

9 1 1

Which toy costs more?

$9

$5

Number the events in the correct order.

2   3   1

Answers on page 316.

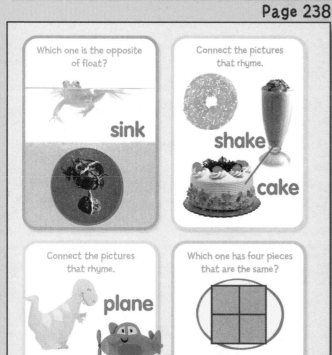

Which one is the opposite of float?

sink

Connect the pictures that rhyme.

shake

cake

Connect the pictures that rhyme.

plane

train

Which one has four pieces that are the same?

Answers on page 316.

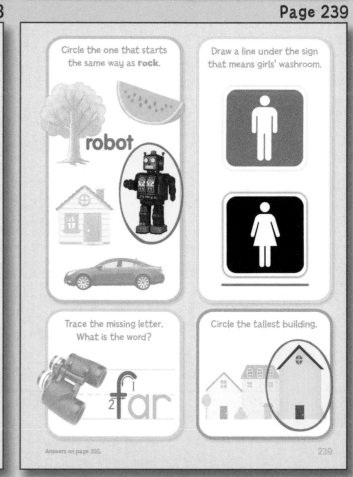

Circle the one that starts the same way as **rock**.

robot

Draw a line under the sign that means girls' washroom.

Trace the missing letter. What is the word?

far

Circle the tallest building.

Answers on page 316.

Answers

Page 240

Which one is a vegetable?

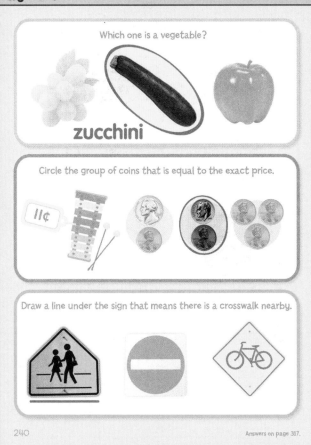

zucchini

Circle the group of coins that is equal to the exact price.

Draw a line under the sign that means there is a crosswalk nearby.

Page 241

Which word means **feet** in Spanish?

pies

regalos

What time is it?

1:00   **5:00**

Circle the animal who is upside-down.

Connect the pictures that rhyme.

bear

pear

Page 242

Read the story, then answer the question.

Snow White

There once was a wicked queen with a magic mirror. It said that Snow White was more beautiful than the queen. Snow White was scared, so she ran into the forest, where she found seven dwarfs living in a cottage. One day, the queen tried to poison Snow White. But a prince saved her and they lived happily ever after.

How many dwarfs did Snow White find in the forest?

5   6   **7**

Page 243

How many nickels?

5

Trace the missing letter. What is the word?

hop

Which food grows above the ground?

tomato

Which word means **kitchen** in Spanish?

cuarto de baño   **cocina**

Solve the subtraction problem.

 5 - 1 = 4

317

Answers

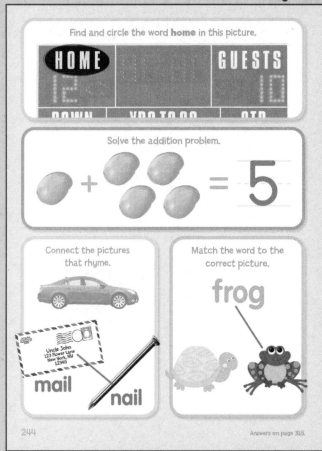

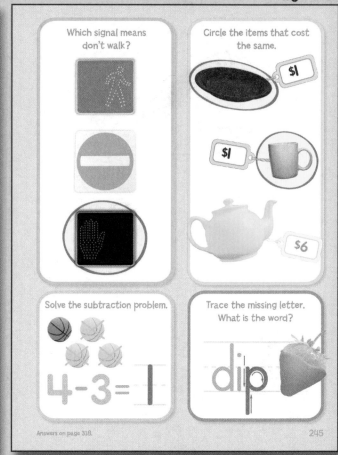

Answers on page 318.

Answers on page 318.

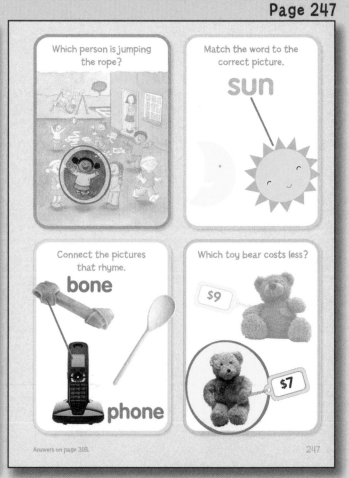

Answers on page 318.

Answers on page 318.

Page 248

Read the nursery rhyme, then answer the questions.

Pease Porridge Hot

Pease porridge hot,
Pease porridge cold,
Pease porridge in the pot,
Nine days old.
Some like it hot,
Some like it cold,
Some like it in the pot,
Nine days old.

How many days old is the porridge?

2 5 (9)

Where is the porridge?

in the pot

Answers on page 319.

Page 249

Connect the pictures that rhyme.

hat

cat

Match the word to the correct picture.

lamb

Number the events in the correct order.

1   3   2

Answers on page 319.   249

Page 250

Which one is a vegetable?

carrot

Solve the subtraction problem.

5 - 3 = 2

Draw a line under the sign that means bicycle crossing.

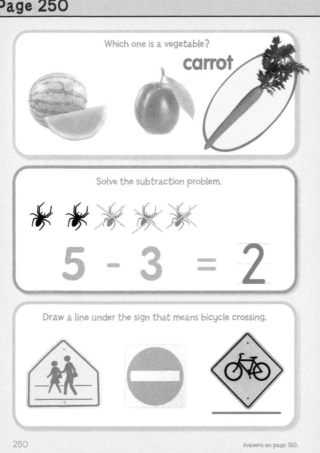

250   Answers on page 319.

Page 251

Circle the smaller cat.

What time is it?

2:00   **(9:00)**

Connect the pictures that rhyme.

barn

yarn

Match the ball to the right equipment.

Answers on page 319.   251

Answers

Number the events in the correct order.

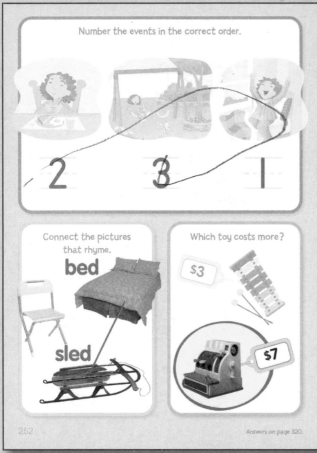

2   3   1

Connect the pictures that rhyme.

bed

sled

Which toy costs more?

$3

$7

Answers on page 320.

Read the story, then answer the question.

Goldilocks and the Three Bears

One day, a little girl named Goldilocks found an empty house that belonged to three bears. She ate their porridge and fell asleep in Baby Bear's bed. The three bears came home and saw that their porridge had been eaten, and that Goldilocks was asleep. Goldilocks woke up, saw the bears, and ran away as fast as she could!

Where did Goldilocks fall asleep?

Baby Bear's bed

Answers on page 320.

Trace the missing letter. What is the word?

hug

Solve the addition problem.

$3 + 2 = 5$

Circle the peppers.

Which one is a star?

sun

Trace the missing letter. What is the word?

win

Answers on page 320.

Which bird is the symbol of America?

bald eagle

Circle the group of coins that is equal to the exact price.

4¢

Circle the letters **S, M, A, R,** and **T** on this keyboard. What do they spell?

Q W E R T Y U I O P
A S D F G H J K L
Z X C V B N M   **SMART**

Answers on page 320.